GRADE
3
Student Workbook

BIBLE CURRICULUM

Walking With God and His People

THIRD
EDITION

ROBIN HUGHES

**CHRISTIAN SCHOOLS
INTERNATIONAL**

GRAND RAPIDS, MICHIGAN

credo
house publishers

Credo House Publishers, Grand Rapids, MI 49525
www.credocommunications.net

Printed in the United States of America

18 17 16 15 14 13 12 11 10 09   2 3 4 5 6 7 8 9 10

ISBN: 978-1-935391-09-8

The development of *Walking With God and His People* was made possible
with grants from Christian Schools International Foundation,
Canadian Christian Education Foundation, Inc., and
Richard & Helen DeVos Foundation.

General Editor: Timothy Beals
Managing Editor: Donna Huisjen
Copyeditor: Elizabeth Banks
Illustrator: Steven Thomason
Cover design: Sharon VanLoozenoord
Interior design and composition: Sharon VanLoozenoord
Bible Dictionary photographs: John and Melanie DeKruyter

Christian Schools International
3350 East Paris Ave SE
Grand Rapids, Michigan 49512-3054

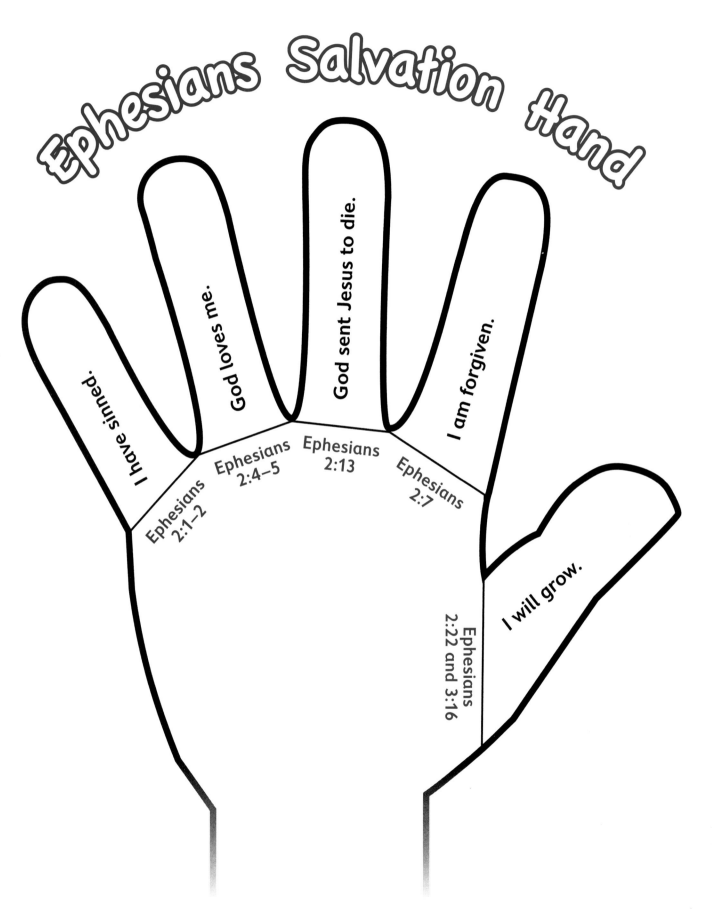

Ephesians Salvation Hand

I have sinned.
Ephesians 2:1–2

God loves me.
Ephesians 2:4–5

God sent Jesus to die.
Ephesians 2:13

I am forgiven.
Ephesians 2:7

I will grow.
Ephesians 2:22 and 3:16

Teamwork Works Best!

From [Christ] the whole body, joined and held together by every supporting ligament, grows and builds itself up in love, as each part does its work.

—Ephesians 4:16

Following Jesus

Follow in the footsteps of Jesus by choosing the right path.

Name

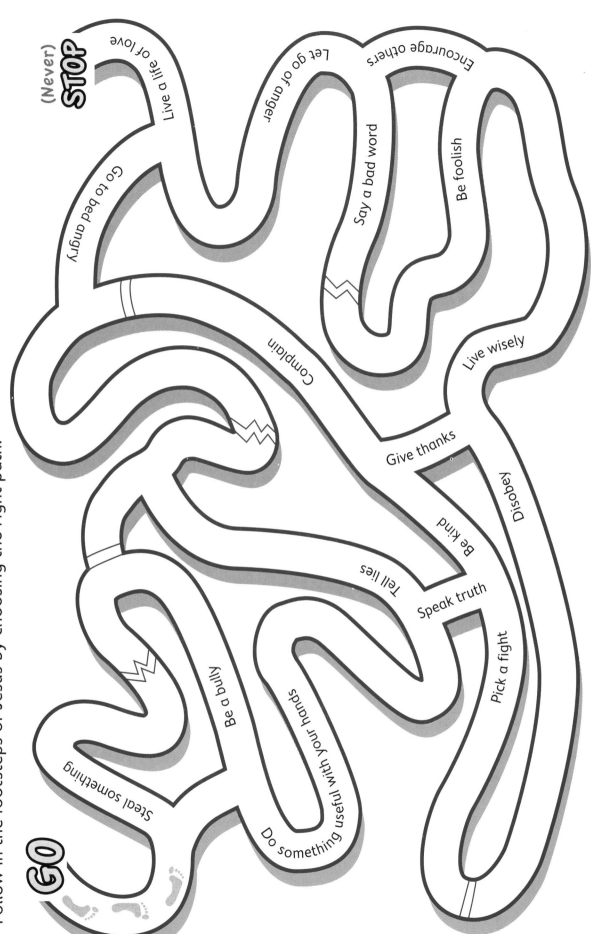

GO

Steal something

Be a bully

Do something useful with your hands

Pick a fight

Speak truth

Be kind

Tell lies

Disobey

Give thanks

Live wisely

Be foolish

Say a bad word

Encourage others

Let go of anger

Complain

Go to bed angry

Live a life of love

(Never) STOP

What Does God Want?

Use the Obedience Decoder to find out what God wants in Ephesians 6:1–2.

```
___ ___ ___ ___ ___ ___ ___ ___ ,   ___ ___ ___ ___
 3   8   9  12   4  18   5  14     15   2   5  25

___ ___ ___ ___    ___ ___ ___ ___ ___ ___ ___    ___ ___
25  15  21  18     16   1  18   5  14  20  19      9  14

___ ___ ___    ___ ___ ___ ___ ,   ___ ___ ___    ___ ___ ___ ___
20   8   5     12  15  18   4      6  15  18      20   8   9  19

                                    "
___ ___    ___ ___ ___ ___ ___ .    ___ ___ ___ ___ ___
 9  19     18   9   7   8  20       8  15  14  15  18

___ ___ ___ ___    ___ ___ ___ ___ ___ ___    ___ ___ ___
25  15  21  18      6   1  20   8   5  18      1  14   4

        "  __
___ ___ ___ ___ ___ ___    ___ ___ ___ ___ ___    ___ ___
13  15  20   8   5  18     23   8   9   3   8      9  19

___ ___ ___    ___ ___ ___ ___ ___
20   8   5      6   9  18  19  20

___ ___ ___ ___ ___ ___ ___ ___ ___ ___ ___
 3  15  13  13   1  14   4  13   5  14  20

___ ___ ___ ___    ___
23   9  20   8     1

___ ___ ___ ___ ___ ___ ___ .
16  18  15  13   9  19   5
```

Look in Ephesians 6:3. Write the promise.

_____

_____

_____

_____

Obedience Decoder			
1	A	14	N
2	B	15	O
3	C	16	P
4	D	17	Q
5	E	18	R
6	F	19	S
7	G	20	T
8	H	21	U
9	I	22	V
10	J	23	W
11	K	24	X
12	L	25	Y
13	M	26	Z

Armor of God

Add each piece of armor from page 11. Then write its name on the line.

Armor of God

Cut out each piece of armor.

Glue each one onto the boy on page 9. Use the given order (1–6).

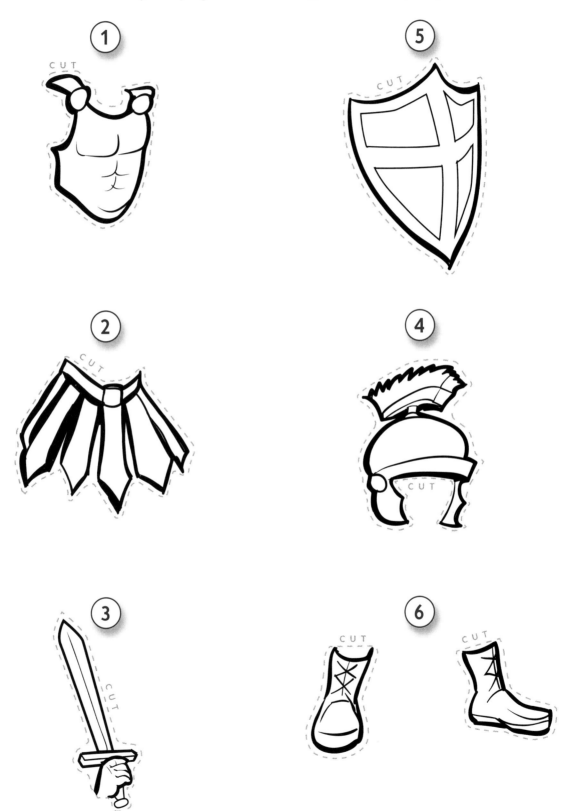

God Talks to Us

Use this phone to decode the verses.

M __ t t h __ __
   2   3 9

4 : 4 b

M __ n d __ __ s n __ t
  2   6 3   6

l __ v __ n b r __ __ d
  4   3   6   3 2

__ l __ n __ , b __ t __ n
2   6   3   8   6

__ v __ r __ w __ r d th __ t
3   3   9   6   2

c __ m __ s f r __ m th __
  6   3   6   3

m __ __ th __ f G __ d .
  6 8   6   6

Use the phone to fill in the missing **vowels** so you can read the verse.

Use the phone to fill in the missing **consonants** so you can read the verse. (This is a bit trickier!)

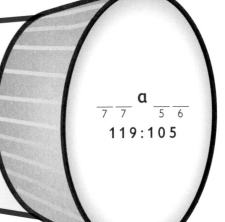

__ o u __ __ o r __ i __ a __ a __ __
9   7 9   3   7   5 6 7

__ o __ y __ e e __ a __ __ a
8   6   3   8   6 3

__ i __ __ __ o __ __ y __ a __ __ .
5 4 4 8   3   7   6   7 8 4

__ __ a __ __
7 7   5 6

119 : 105

God's Library

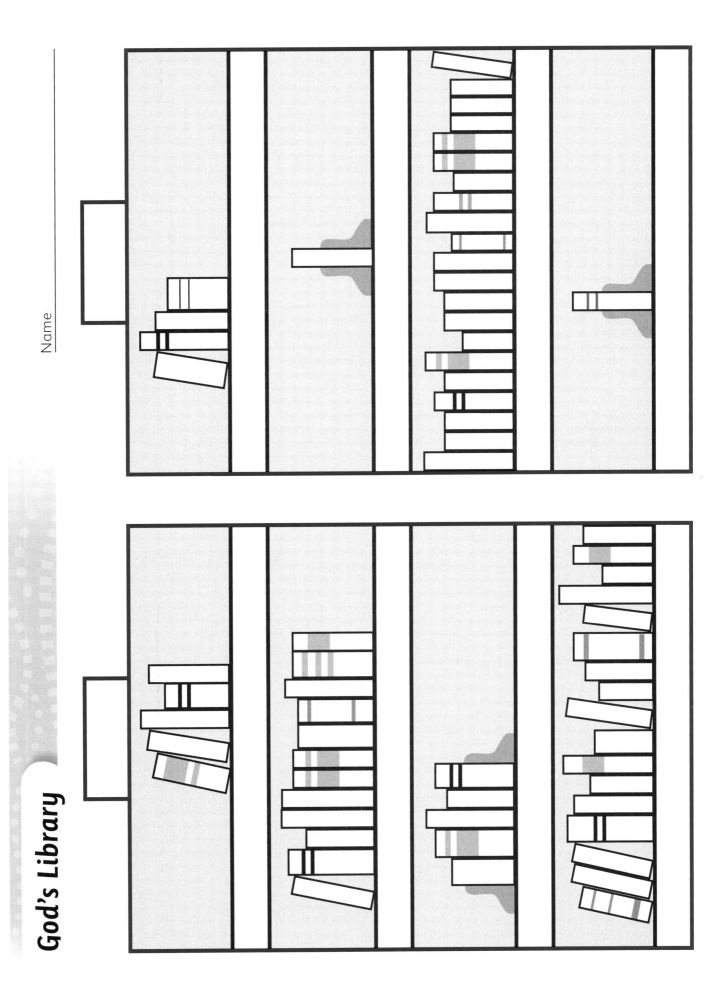

About the Bible

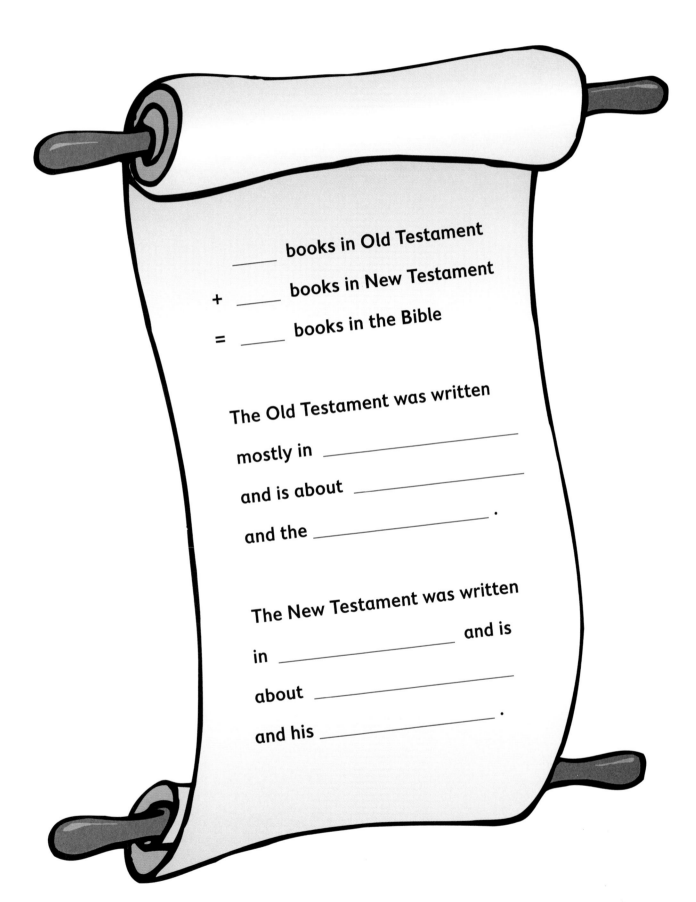

_____ books in Old Testament

+ _____ books in New Testament

= _____ books in the Bible

The Old Testament was written

mostly in _____

and is about _____

and the _____ .

The New Testament was written

in _____ and is

about _____

and his _____ .

Mini Bible Concordance

COMMANDMENT

Joshua 22:5 "But be very careful to keep the commandment and the law that Moses the servant of the LORD gave you: to love the LORD your God, to walk in all his ways, to obey his commands, to hold fast to him and to serve him with all your heart and all your soul."

Matthew 22:37–40 Jesus replied: "'Love the Lord your God with all your heart and with all your soul and with all your mind.' This is the first and greatest commandment. And the second is like it: 'Love your neighbor as yourself.' All the Law and the Prophets hang on these two commandments."

DAVID

1 Samuel 16:23 Whenever the spirit from God came upon Saul, David would take his harp and play. Then relief would come to Saul.

2 Samuel 5:4 David was thirty years old when he became king, and he reigned forty years.

FAITH

Ephesians 2:8 For it is by grace you have been saved, through faith—and this not from yourselves, it is the gift of God.

Hebrews 12:2 Let us fix our eyes on Jesus, the author and perfecter of our faith, who for the joy set before him endured the cross, scorning its shame, and sat down at the right hand of the throne of God.

FAMINE

Genesis 41:30 But seven years of famine will follow them. Then all the abundance in Egypt will be forgotten, and the famine will ravage the land.

1 Kings 18:2 So Elijah went to present himself to Ahab. Now the famine was severe in Samaria.

JACOB

Genesis 32:28 Then the man said, "Your name will no longer be Jacob, but Israel, because you have struggled with God and with men and have overcome."

JESUS

Matthew 1:21–23 "She will give birth to a son, and you are to give him the name Jesus, because he will save his people from their sins." All this took place to fulfill what the Lord had said through the prophet: "The virgin will be with child and will give birth to a son, and they will call him Immanuel"—which means, "God with us."

John 8:12 When Jesus spoke again to the people, he said, "I am the light of the world. Whoever follows me will never walk in darkness, but will have the light of life."

John 10:7, 11 Therefore Jesus said again, "I tell you the truth, I am the gate for the sheep. . . . I am the good shepherd. The good shepherd lays down his life for the sheep."

MORIAH

Genesis 22:2 Then God said, "Take your son, your only son, Isaac, whom you love, and go to the region of Moriah. Sacrifice him there as a burnt offering on one of the mountains I will tell you about."

2 Chronicles 3:1 Then Solomon began to build the temple of the LORD in Jerusalem on Mount Moriah, where the LORD had appeared to his father David. It was on the threshing floor of Araunah.

NOAH

Genesis 6:10 Noah had three sons: Shem, Ham and Japheth.

Genesis 7:6 Noah was six hundred years old when the floodwaters came on the earth.

PASSOVER

Deuteronomy 16:2–3 Sacrifice as the Passover to the LORD your God an animal from your flock or herd at the place the LORD will choose as a dwelling for his Name. Do not eat it with bread made with yeast, but for seven days eat unleavened bread, the bread of affliction, becuase you left Egypt in haste—so that all the days of your life you may remember the time of your departure from Egypt.

PAUL

Acts 15:36 Some time later Paul said to Barnabas, "Let us go back and visit the brothers in all the towns where we preached the word of the Lord and see how they are doing."

Acts 16:19 When the owners of the slave girl realized that their hope of making money was gone, they seized Paul and Silas and dragged them into the marketplace to face the authorities.

Acts 18:18 Paul stayed on in Corinth for some time. Then he left the brothers and sailed for Syria, accompanied by Priscilla and Aquila. Before he sailed, he had his hair cut off at Cenchrea because of a vow he had taken.

Concordance Worksheet

Underline the key word that you need to look up in the mini Bible concordance. Then look up the word and find the verse to answer each question.

1. What musical instrument did David play? _____

_____

2. What new name did God give to Jacob? _____

_____

3. How old was Noah when the flood began? _____

_____

4. What did Jesus consider to be the second greatest commandment? _____

_____

_____

5. What important building was constructed on Mount Moriah? _____

_____

6. Who is the author and perfecter of our faith? _____

_____

7. What kind of bread did the Israelites eat when they celebrated the Passover feast? _____

_____

8. List two other names for Jesus. _____

_____

_____

9. List two places that had a famine. _____

_____

10. List two people who traveled with Paul on his journeys. _____

_____

CUT

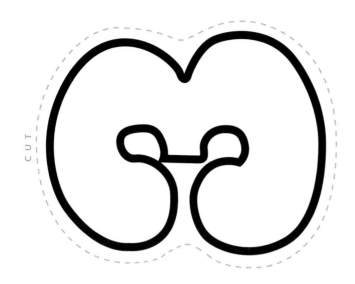

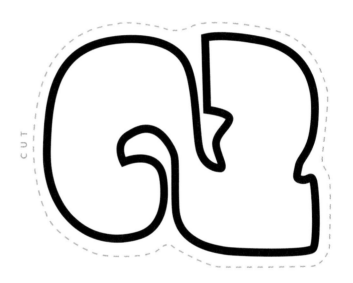

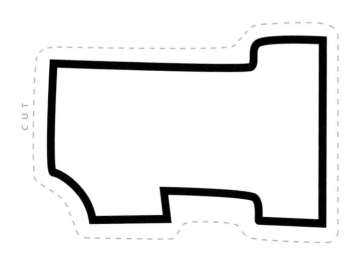

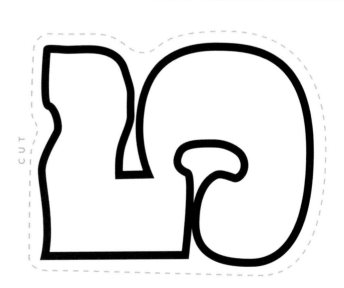

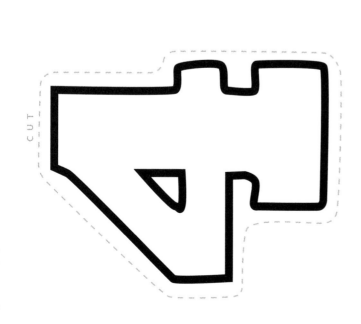

CUT

Creation Riddle Puzzle

Answer the questions about creation to fill in the crossword puzzle.

Across

1. God planted a garden in my eastern section. What am I? (Genesis 2:8)

_____

3. God made me from dust. Who am I? (Genesis 2:7) _____

5. I was the third river. What's my name? (Genesis 2:14) _____

Down

1. I was the fourth river. What's my name? (Genesis 2:14; 3:20)

_____

2. I was made from a rib. Who am I? (Genesis 2:22) _____

4. I'm the Tree of Knowledge of Good and Evil. Where in the garden am I? (Genesis 2:9) _____

Sins to Avoid

On each side of the snake, write the sins you will avoid. Then decorate the snake.

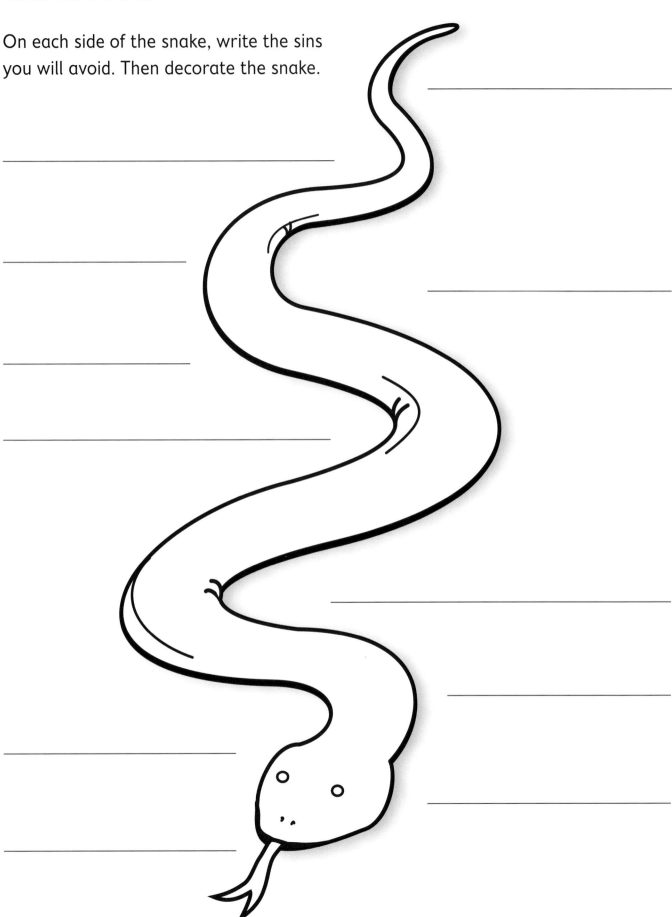

Cain and Abel

Look in Genesis 4 to find the correct word to fill in each puzzle clue.
Then unscramble the circled letters to complete the sentence below the puzzles.

God accepted Abel's offering because Abel's offering came from his

____ ____ ____ ____ ____ .

Down

1. Cain said that his _____
   was more than he could bear. (v. 13)
3. God looked with favor on
   Abel's _____ . (v. 4)
4. _____ brought an offering
   from his flock. (v. 4)

Across

2. Cain worked the _____ . (v. 2)
5. Cain went away to live in _____ . (v. 16)
6. Cain didn't think he was his brother's
   _____ . (v. 9)
7. Abel kept _____ . (v. 2)
8. _____ was very angry. (v. 5)
9. Cain _____ Abel. (v. 8)

Family Tree

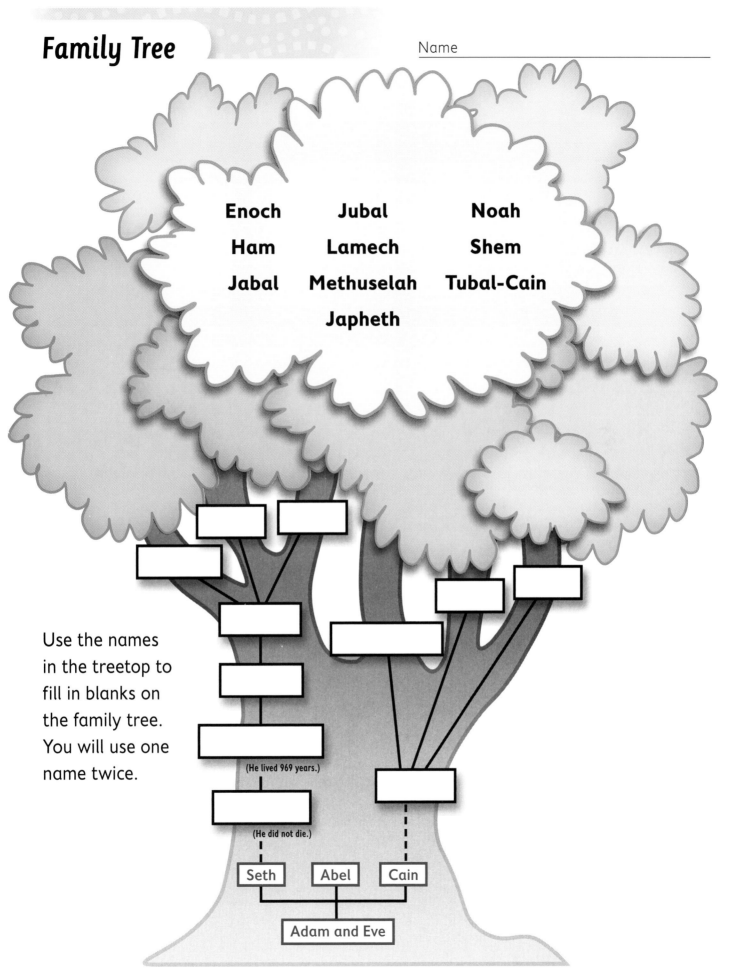

Enoch   Jubal   Noah

Ham   Lamech   Shem

Jabal   Methuselah   Tubal-Cain

Japheth

Use the names in the treetop to fill in blanks on the family tree. You will use one name twice.

(He lived 969 years.)

(He did not die.)

Seth   Abel   Cain

Adam and Eve

Noah Builds the Ark

Narrator 1: God looked down at all that he had created and saw that it was no longer good.

Narrator 2: God saw how wicked people had become.

Narrator 3: He saw that people's thoughts were evil. So were their hearts.

Narrator 4: God was sorry that he had made people. He was ready to destroy the earth.

Narrator 5: But as God looked at his creation, he found one man who obeyed him and loved only him.

Narrator 1: Only Noah walked with the Lord and did what was right in God's eyes.

Narrator 2: God told Noah that he was going to destroy the world because it had grown so evil and violent.

Narrator 3: God told Noah to build an ark. Noah, his family, and some of God's creatures would be saved.

Narrator 4: Noah listened to God. Right away he began to build the large boat, just as God had commanded.

Narrator 5: Noah's neighbors saw what Noah was building, and they thought that he was crazy.

Neighbor 1: Hey, Noah, what are you building over there?

Neighbor 2: Are you adding some rooms to your house?

Noah: No. I'm building an ark. God told me to build it.

Neighbor 3: A what?

Noah's Wife:	He's building an ark. You know—a big boat.
Neighbor 4:	Are you crazy? The only water around here is the stream flowing behind the village.
Neighbor 5:	How are you going to haul that big thing to the sea? There's no way!
Neighbor 6:	You'd need all of the donkeys in the village to pull your ark even a foot.
Neighbor 3:	I really don't want to spend the rest of my life looking out my kitchen window at your ugly, worthless boat.
Neighbor 2:	I agree. It's unfair to expect us to stare at that big boat every day!
Neighbor 4:	We moved into the neighborhood because of the beautiful fields and houses. Now you think that you can ruin it by deciding to build an ark.
Noah's Wife:	He didn't decide to build an ark. God commanded him to build an ark.
Neighbors:	Who?
Noah's Wife:	God.
Neighbors:	Who's that?
Noah:	Don't you know who God is?
Neighbors:	No.
Noah:	God created everything in this world. He made you, me, and all of the animals. God provides for our needs by sending rain and sunshine for our fields, and . . .
Neighbor 6:	You mean Mother Nature, don't you?
Noah and Noah's Wife:	Who?
Neighbor 6:	Mother Nature.
Noah and Noah's Wife:	Who's that?

Neighbor 2:	Never mind. They don't get it.
Neighbor 5:	I really don't expect them to. After all, they're building an ark for a God they can't even see.
Neighbor 3:	Let's get out of here. I want to get ready for the big party tonight.
Neighbor 1:	You know it's going to be fun. The only rule is to have fun.
Neighbor 6:	Remember last time? We ended up letting all his cattle and sheep out of their pens. Now that was a good time!
Noah's Wife:	Noah, God's right. This is an evil, sinful world.
Noah:	I can't believe that our neighbors don't even know about God.
Noah's Wife:	We'd better get going. I can see why God's patience has run out with his sinful creation.
Noah:	I think that we'll be finished building in about 120 years, and then God will send the animals.
Noah's Wife:	It's not going to be easy caring for all those animals in the ark.
Noah:	God never said it would be easy. But he did say he'd be with us!
Narrator 1:	Noah and his family worked until they had finished building the ark and its three decks.
Narrator 2:	God sent to the ark at least two of every kind of bird, animal, and creature that moved along the ground.
Narrator 3:	Noah and his family stored up food for both themselves and the animals to eat.
Narrator 4:	Noah did all that God commanded him. He, along with his family, entered the ark.
Narrator 5:	After seven days, God opened the flood waters of the earth and heaven.
Narrator 1:	It rained for 40 days and nights. Every living thing on the earth was wiped out, but Noah and his family were saved.

God's Rainbow Covenant

Find Genesis 9:12–13 in your NIV Bible. Fill in the blanks to review God's promise.

And _____ said, "This is the _____ of the _____

I am making between me and you and every living _____ with you,

a covenant for all _____ to come: I have _____ my

_____ in the _____ , and it will be the sign of the covenant

_____ me and the _____ .

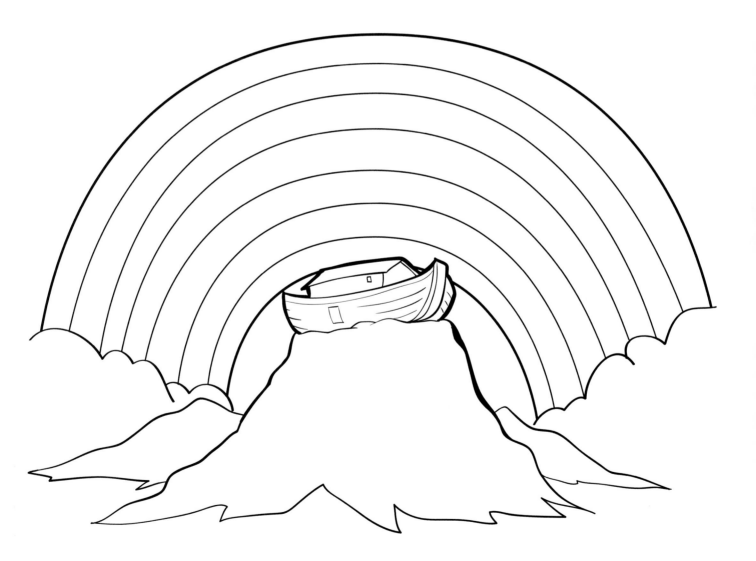

The Tower of Babel

After the flood, many years passed. More people were born. A group of these people moved east to a plain in the land of Shinar, which was later called Babylon. They decided to build a large tower that would reach the heavens. This tower was probably a **ziggurat**. A ziggurat was a temple tower common in the land of Babylon. It was the place where people came to worship their gods. Ziggurats looked like pyramids, but they didn't have smooth sides. Most ziggurats had seven stories. Each story was a little smaller than the one below it, which made it look like steps. There were stairways on the outside of the building that connected each level. Some ziggurats were cone-shaped and had stairs or ramps that wound around the tower leading to the top. Other ziggurats had four levels.

These ziggurats were large buildings. They were usually about 300 feet high. The Tower of Babel was one of the largest ziggurats. Each level was painted a different color, which made the building look like a huge rainbow! Mud-brick was the common building material. It was made of either mud and straw or clay. Then it was fired at high heat to make it very strong. Asphalt was used instead of mortar to hold the bricks together.

Here are the colors for a seven-layered ziggurat:

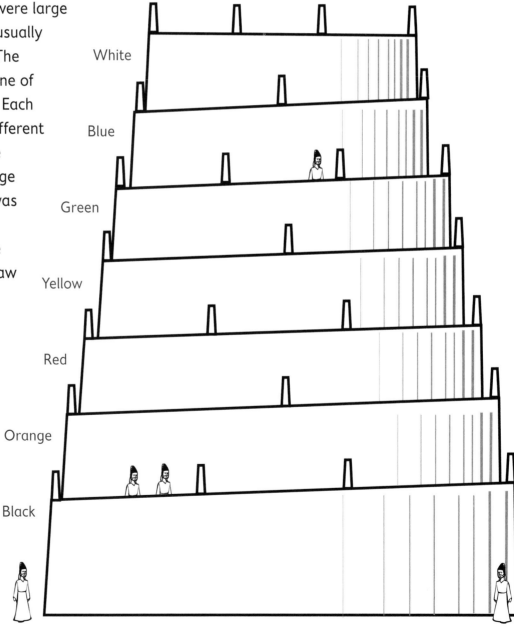

White

Blue

Green

Yellow

Red

Orange

Black

Moving Day

Imagine that you and your family are moving to another city. Instead of hiring a moving truck, you are going to walk with all of your possessions to your new home. It will take you a whole month to walk there. Your parents have decided that you can take along only what will fit into your wagon. In the wagon below draw all of the items you will need to take along. Don't forget that you will also need to fit your clothes, pillow, and blankets in your wagon. Don't fill it so full that you can't pull it!

Name _____

Abraham's Journey to Canaan

Ur

Tigris River

Euphrates River

Haran

Great
Sea

Shechem
Bethel
Ai
CANAAN
NEGEV

EGYPT

Red Sea

NORTH

0   40   80 100 mi.
0 40   80 120 km.

God's Promises to Abraham

Fill in the blanks with the correct words. Use Genesis 12:2–3, 7 and the word bank at the bottom of the page to find the answers.

"I will make you into a _____

    and I will _____ ;

I will make your _____ ,

    and you will be a _____ .

I will _____ who bless you,

and whoever curses you

    _____ ;

and all peoples on earth

    will be _____ .

To your offspring I will _____ ."

Word Bank			
blessed through you	give this land	blessing	great nation
bless those	I will curse	bless you	name great

Lot's Choice

Lot made the selfish choice of choosing the best land for himself. In the boxes below draw a comic strip about Lot's choice.

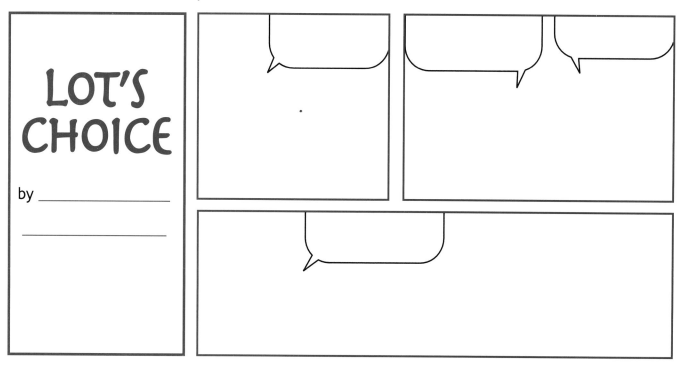

Lot made his choice because he thought it would make his life easier. Sometimes doing the right thing can be hard. In the boxes below draw a comic strip about a choice a Christian should make.

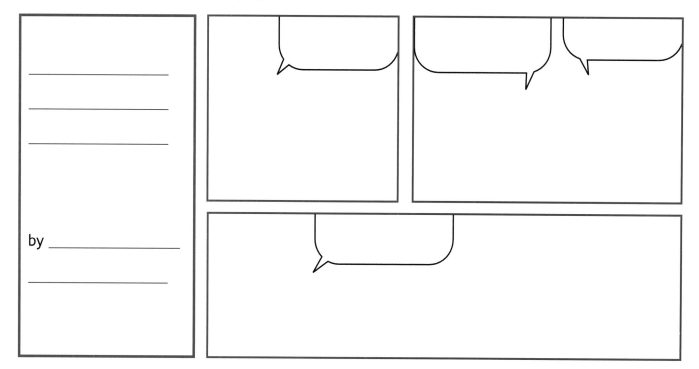

Abram, Sarai, and Hagar

Write a diary entry for Abram, Sarai, or Hagar. Imagine that today Hagar has arrived back at her tent after running away. Write what Abram, Sarai, or Hagar must have thought about the past events and the coming birth of Ishmael. Use the word "I" in your entry to make it seem more like Abram, Sarai, or Hagar wrote it.

Dear Diary

_____

_____

_____

_____

_____

_____

_____

_____

_____

_____

_____

God's Covenant with Abraham

God made a covenant, or agreement, with Abraham. He promised, "I will be your God. You and your children will be my people." God also made other promises to Abraham and Sarah's children. In the boxes draw pictures or symbols that show God's promises to Abraham.

To have kings come from Abraham's children

To change Abram and Sarai's names to Abraham and Sarah

To make Abraham the father of many nations

To give Abraham's children the land of Canaan

To give Sarah a son in a year

Abraham had to obey God. God told Abraham to:
- walk before God.
- keep the agreement or covenant by having all males in his household circumcised, a sign that they belonged to the covenant.

Your New Name

Imagine that you were to change your name to reflect your dedication to God. You want to choose a name that reflects your relationship with God. Maybe your parents already thought about this when they named you. They may have chosen your name because of its meaning.

Look through the names listed on the right or through a book with names for babies, and choose a "new" name. If your name already has special meaning, you may choose to keep it. You will have to explain how this name reflects your relationship with God.

Name _____

Boys

Aaron "To sing"
Christopher "Christ-bearer"
Daniel "God is my judge"
Dominique "Of God"
Elijah "The Lord is my God"
Gabriel "God is my strength"
Isaiah "Salvation of God"
Jaden "God has heard"
Jeremy "God will uplift"
Joel "God is willing"
Josiah "Fire of the Lord"
Matthew "Gift of God"
Nathaniel "Gift of God"
Samuel "God has heard"
Timothy "To honor God"
Zachary "Remembrance
        of the Lord"

Girls

Adalia "God is my refuge"
Aletha "Truthful one"
Amelia "Work of the Lord"
Amy "Beloved"
Christine "Christ-bearer"
Dorothy "Gift of God"
Elisabeth "Consecrated to God"
Grace "Grace of God"
Hannah "Grace of God"
Isabel "Consecrated to God"
Janelle "God is gracious"
Jorryn "The one God loves"
Kiah "God is strength"
Kwanita "God is gracious"
Moriah "God is my teacher"
Thea "Gift of God"

name

The name I have chosen is _____

That name means _____

I chose this name because _____

Three Visitors: Part 1

Setting: Abraham is standing outside his tent as three men approach. Sarah is working inside the tent.

Narrator 1:	One hot day, when Abraham was sitting at the door of his tent, he looked up and saw three men standing nearby. (Abraham hurries to meet them and bows low to the ground.)
Abraham:	If I have found favor in your eyes, my lord, do not pass me by. My servants will bring some water so that you may all wash your feet. Rest under this tree. I'll get you something to eat before you go on your way.
Visitors:	Thank you.
Abraham:	Sarah, please bake some bread. We have guests.
Narrator 2:	Abraham told a servant to prepare meat. Abraham got some curds and milk.
Narrator 3:	When the food was ready, he served it to the visitors.
Visitors:	Where is Sarah, your wife?
Abraham:	She's in the tent. (Sarah cups her ear, listening when she hears her name.)
Voice of the Lord:	I will return to you about this time next year. By then Sarah, your wife, will have a son.
Narrator 4:	Sarah was listening at the door to the tent.
Narrator 5:	Abraham and Sarah were already old, so Sarah laughed at the thought of having a child.
Sarah (laughing):	Will I really have a child now that I'm old?
Voice of the Lord:	Why did Sarah laugh and say, "Will I really have a child, now that I am old?" Is anything too hard for the Lord? Next year Sarah will have a son.
Sarah (afraid):	I didn't laugh.
Voice of the Lord:	Yes, you did laugh.

Foods from Bible Times

Name _____

Look up the Bible passages to fill in this crossword puzzle about the eating customs of nomads.

ACROSS

2. This was prepared for Abraham's guests. (Genesis 18:7)

5. Hagar took some _____ in a skin into the wilderness. (Genesis 21:14)

7. Abraham's guests were given _____ to drink. (Genesis 18:8)

8. Lot prepared bread without _____ because he was in a hurry. (Genesis 19:3)

DOWN

1. Sarah prepared this for Abraham's guests. (Genesis 18:6)

3. People washed their _____ before the meal. (Genesis 18:4)

4. Abraham's guests were also given _____ . (Genesis 18:8)

6. Melchizedek gave Abram bread and _____ . (Genesis 14:18)

Three Visitors: Part 2

Name _____

Setting: Abraham is standing outside his tent with his visitors as they start to leave.

Narrator 1:	When Abraham's visitors were ready to leave, Abraham walked along with them to see them on their way. (Abraham and the visitors walk a few steps away.)
Narrator 2:	As they looked down toward the city of Sodom, the Lord told Abraham what he was going to do.
Voice of the Lord:	Abraham, the cities of Sodom and Gomorrah are wicked.
Narrator 3:	The visitors went on toward Sodom, but Abraham remained standing before the Lord. (The three visitors walk off stage.)
Abraham:	If you decide to destroy the cities, will you destroy the good with the wicked? What if 50 good people are found in the city? Will you really sweep it away and not spare the place for the sake of the 50 righteous people? Will not the Judge of all the earth do right?
Voice of the Lord:	If I find 50 good people in the city of Sodom, I will spare the whole place.
Abraham:	What if the number of good people is 5 less than 50? Will you destroy the whole city because of 5 people?
Voice of the Lord:	If I find 45 there, I will not destroy it.
Abraham:	What if only 40 are found there?
Voice of the Lord:	For the sake of 40, I will not destroy it.
Abraham:	Please don't be angry, but let me speak. What if only 30 good people are in that city?
Voice of the Lord:	I will not destroy it if I find 30 there.
Abraham:	I have been very bold to speak to the Lord. Now I have to ask, what if only 20 can be found in Sodom?
Voice of the Lord:	For the sake of 20, I will not destroy it.
Abraham:	May the Lord not be angry—but let me speak just one more time. What if you find only 10 good people in Sodom?
Voice of the Lord:	For the sake of 10, I will not destroy it.
Narrator 4:	When the Lord had finished speaking with Abraham, he left, and Abraham returned home.

Genesis 17:7–9

Name _____

Find and circle words from Genesis 17:7–9 in the word search puzzle. The words might be across, down, or diagonal. Then use those words to fill in the blanks. You will use some of the words more than once.

T	S	G	A	W	I	Y	G	U	D	R	M	E	H	N
Y	D	L	O	E	R	M	O	M	J	V	S	C	A	Y
T	T	O	N	D	V	E	H	P	W	T	U	A	A	B
A	E	B	O	D	D	E	Q	O	N	O	N	Q	A	F
P	U	F	Q	M	M	N	R	A	Y	A	J	E	F	H
F	Q	O	J	I	G	G	D	L	C	Y	E	G	K	P
C	S	F	D	Q	T	N	T	A	A	Y	S	L	N	T
N	F	C	P	U	E	N	V	W	B	S	J	D	Q	B
U	B	R	B	C	A	K	M	R	H	R	T	F	K	D
T	X	X	S	N	T	U	L	D	X	F	A	I	N	S
U	T	E	E	W	V	U	F	P	E	Y	V	H	N	S
T	D	V	D	O	D	T	H	K	L	E	H	Z	A	G
W	O	G	L	M	M	K	U	B	I	C	B	N	Q	M
C	T	H	Y	U	R	P	P	L	B	C	B	A	K	N
G	E	N	E	R	A	T	I	O	N	S	J	I	U	Z

"'I will establish my _____ as an _____ _____

between me and you and your _____ after you for the _____ to come,

to be your _____ and the _____ of your _____ after

you. The whole land of _____ , where you are now an alien, I will give as

an _____ possession to _____ and your _____ after

you; and I will be their _____ .'

   "Then _____ said to _____ , 'As for you, you must keep my

_____ , you and your _____ after you for the _____

to come.'"

Abraham's Family

Read the story below. Choose the word from the word bank that fits best in each blank. Then fill in the blanks in the correct spaces below.

God told _____ (4) to leave Ur and go to a place that God would show him. God made a _____ (10) with Abram, promising Abram many descendants. God promised that his descendants would be a blessing to all _____ (1).

Because Sarai and Abram didn't have any children, Sarai gave _____ (2) to Abram as a wife. Hagar had a son named _____ (5).

One day _____ (3) appeared to Abraham and told him that Sarah would have a son. They should name him _____ (6). When the baby was born, he brought _____ (7) to his old parents.

When Ishmael made fun of Isaac, _____ (9) told Abraham to send him away. Hagar and Ishmael wandered in the _____ (8). They were ready to die when an _____ (11) of God appeared to Hagar and showed her where to find water.

Write here who Isaac was.
(The answer is in the puzzle.)

_____

Word Bank			
Abram	desert	Isaac	people
angel	God	Ishmael	Sarah
covenant	Hagar	laughter	

Who Am I?

Write a riddle for Abraham, Isaac, or Sarah. Think of what you know about the person you have chosen. Then finish each sentence as if you were that person. Be descriptive when you write your sentences.

I am _____.

I see _____

_____.

I hear _____

_____.

I want _____

_____.

I worry _____

_____.

I cry _____

_____.

I say _____

_____.

I dream _____

_____.

I hope _____

_____.

Jacob and Esau: The Birthright

Name _____

Unscramble the words to the left of each blank. Write the word on the blank. Then answer the questions below.

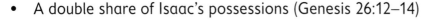

Esau traded his birthright. This included . . .

- A double share of Isaac's possessions (Genesis 26:12–14)

  sproc   _____   (verse 12)

  lkofcs   _____   (verse 14)

  drshe   _____   (verse 14)

  nvatsres   _____   (verse 14)

- God's promises (Genesis 26:3–5)

  alnd   _____   (verse 3)

  scnedtnaeds   _____   (verse 4)

  sbenislg   _____ to all nations (verse 4)

He traded all of this for a bowl of . . .

  eitlselnwt   _____ _____   (Genesis 25:34)

1. Do you think that Esau made a good trade? _____

   _____

2. What does this trade show about Esau? _____

   _____

   _____

   _____

3. Who did God want to have the birthright? _____

   _____

Isaac and Abimelech

Look up each verse in your Bible to find the answers for the puzzle. (All of the answers are in Genesis 26.)

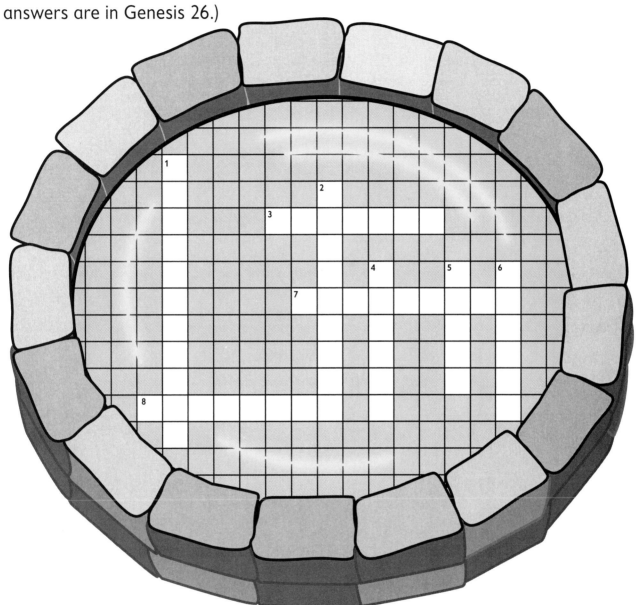

Across

3. Whom did Isaac say was his sister? (v. 7)

7. Where was Isaac when he built an altar, pitched his tent, and dug a well? (vv. 23–25)

8. What did Isaac name the well where no one quarreled? (v. 22)

Down

1. Who stopped up the wells with earth? (v. 15)

2. Who was the king of the Philistines in Gerar? (v. 1)

4. What was the sworn agreement that Isaac made with Abimelech called? (v. 28)

5. What was the name of the valley Isaac moved to when Abimelech sent him away? (v. 17)

6. What caused Isaac to go to Gerar? (v. 1)

Jacob at the Well

Name _____

Imagine that you are going to direct a play about Jacob meeting Rachel at the well. As a group, you need to decide on the following items for your play.

1. What costumes will Jacob and Rachel wear? Will they wear certain colors? Will they be wearing jewelry? Will their clothes be old or new?

_____

_____

_____

_____

2. What will your set look like? Will there be trees? How large will the well be? Will you use live animals, or will people dress up in animal costumes?

_____

_____

_____

_____

3. What will Jacob and Rachel look and sound like? Will they be old or young? Will they have loud voices or soft voices? What hairstyles will they have?

_____

_____

_____

_____

4. What types of sounds will there be during the play: animals, other people talking, wind?

_____

_____

_____

_____

Jacob's Story

Use words from the word bank to fill in the blanks in his story.
Then draw a picture of one of the things that happened to Jacob.

My name is Jacob. My father's

name is _____ , and my mother's name

is _____ . I have a twin brother named

_____ . One day Esau was very

hungry, and he sold his _____ to

me for a bowl of lentil stew. Later, with my

mother's help, I tricked my father into giving

me the _____ . Esau was very _____

with me for stealing the blessing. I had to

run away because I was afraid that he would

kill me. I went to _____ . There I

worked for my uncle _____ . First

I married his daughter _____ , and

then I married _____ .

Word Bank		
angry	Haran	Leah
birthright	Isaac	Rachel
blessing	Laban	Rebekah
	Esau	

Jacob's Sons

Name _____

Draw a line from each son to his mother. The meaning of each son's name is printed under his name.

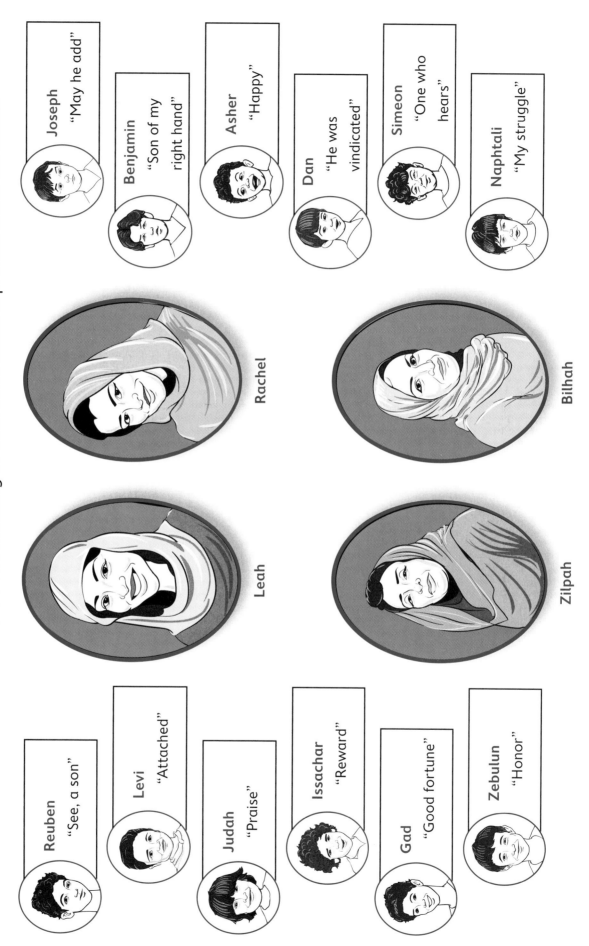

Joseph
"May he add"

Benjamin
"Son of my right hand"

Asher
"Happy"

Dan
"He was vindicated"

Simeon
"One who hears"

Naphtali
"My struggle"

Rachel

Bilhah

Leah

Zilpah

Reuben
"See, a son"

Levi
"Attached"

Judah
"Praise"

Issachar
"Reward"

Gad
"Good fortune"

Zebulun
"Honor"

Jacob Flees from Laban

Imagine that you were able to write a letter to Laban, Jacob, Rachel, or Leah. What questions would you ask them? Are there people whom you would like to ask them about? Are there events in their lives that you'd like to know more about?

Write your letter.
Make sure to include which person you are writing to, and to sign your name at the end.

_____

_____

_____

_____

_____

_____

_____

_____

_____

_____

_____

_____

_____

_____

Jacob's Life

Number the signs and draw arrows from sign to sign to show the order of events in Jacob's life. The first and last signs are numbered for you.

1 Esau and Jacob were born.

Esau sold Jacob his birthright.

Rebekah and Jacob tricked Isaac into blessing Jacob.

God appeared to Jacob in a dream.

Jacob ran away from Esau.

Jacob married Rachel.

God wrestled with Jacob.

Jacob married Leah.

Jacob had many children and became rich.

11 Jacob returned to Canaan.

Jacob ran away from Laban.

A Family Reunion

Name _____

Jacob traveled many miles to reach Canaan. Fill in the blanks below. Then trace Jacob's journey from Haran to his home in Canaan.

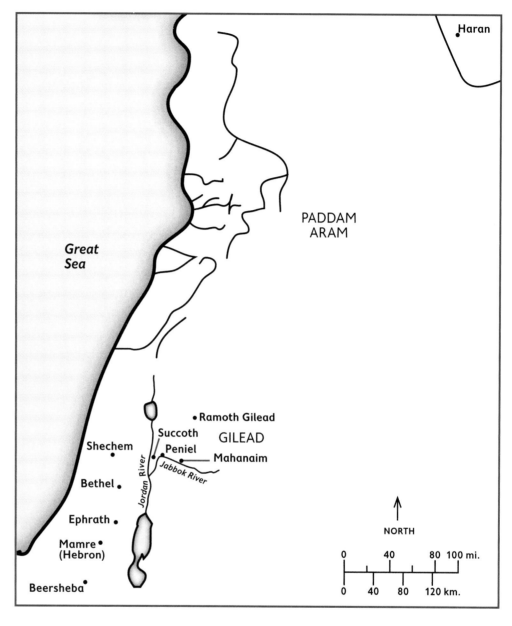

1. Jacob started his journey in _____ .

2. Laban caught up to Jacob in the hill country of _____ . (Genesis 31:23)

3. The angels of God met Jacob in a place he later named _____ . (Genesis 32:1–2)

4. Jacob and his children crossed the _____ at night before meeting Esau. (Genesis 32:22)

5. Jacob called the place where he wrestled with God _____ . (Genesis 32:30)

6. Jacob did not follow Esau to Seir; instead, he went to _____ . (Genesis 33:17)

7. Later, Jacob bought a plot of land near the city of _____ . (Genesis 33:18–20)

Dream Number _____
Dreamed by _____

Interpretation of Dream:

Dream Number _____
Dreamed by _____

Interpretation of Dream:

Do Over

Pretend you are Joseph or one of his brothers. Write a journal entry that tells how you feel now that the day is over and Joseph has been sold as a slave. Tell what you would do differently if you could relive the day.

Egypt Project Reports

Name _____

1. Topic: _____

2. Books used: _____

   _____

   _____

3. Notes about topic: _____

   _____

   _____

   _____

4. Possible main ideas: _____

   _____

5. Main ideas for report: _____

   _____

   _____

6. Details that will tell about the main idea: _____

   _____

   _____

   _____

   _____

   _____

   _____

   _____

   _____

   _____

   _____

7. Pictures for oral report: _____

   _____

(Use lined paper or index cards for more notes.)

Dream Number ____ ____

Dreamed by ____

Interpretation of Dream:

Dream Number ____ ____

Dreamed by ____

Interpretation of Dream:

Dream Number _____

Dreamed by _____

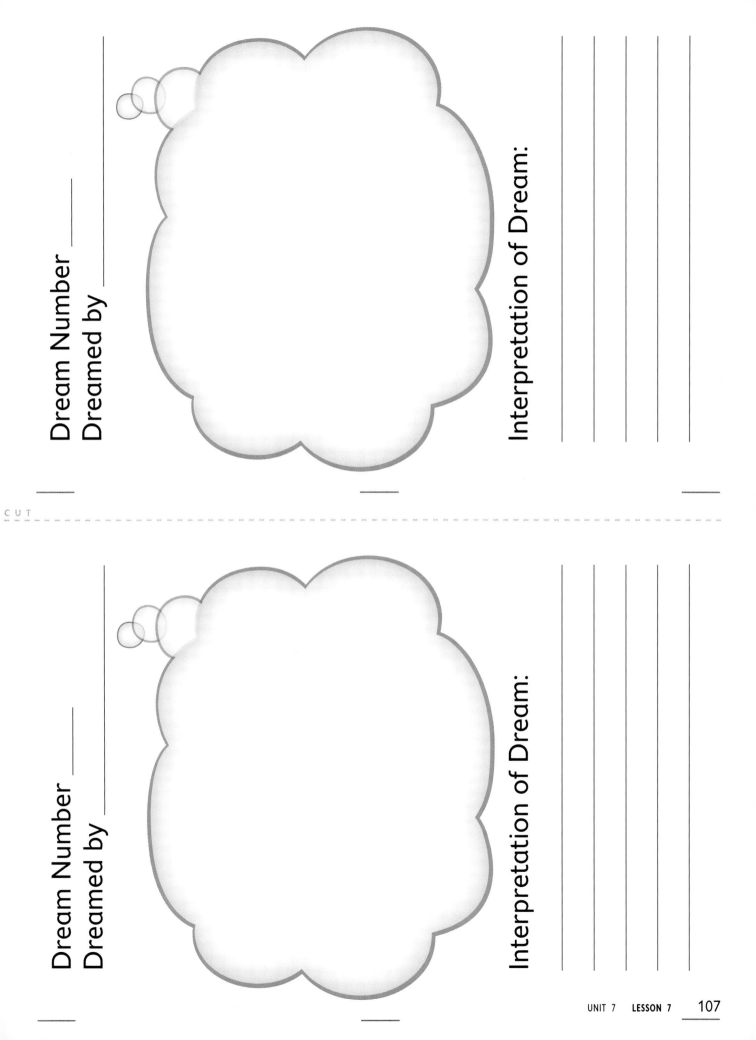

Interpretation of Dream:

Dream Number _____

Dreamed by _____

Interpretation of Dream:

CUT

Joseph's Brothers Arrive in Egypt

Narrator 1:   The famine had spread through the countries near Egypt.

Narrator 2:   Jacob and his family didn't have very much food left, but grain was for sale in Egypt.

Narrator 3:   He called his sons to his tent.

Jacob: It's easy to see that we will not have a crop again this year. But I have good news! Some men from the caravan that just left told me that there is food in Egypt. Here are some silver coins. Take the money, and go to Egypt to buy food.

Benjamin: Yes, Father. We'd be glad to.

Jacob: Wait a minute, Benjamin. You won't be going.

Benjamin: What do you mean? I'm almost 30 years old!

Jacob: Joseph is dead, and I couldn't live if something bad happened to you.

Reuben: Yes, stay here, Benjamin, and take care of our families for us. We'll be back as soon as we can.

Narrator 4:   The brothers set out from Canaan and traveled to Egypt.

Narrator 5:   When they arrived in Egypt, they couldn't believe their eyes.

Narrator 1:   The storehouses were spilling over with grain.

Narrator 2:   The brothers set up a meeting with the governor so that they could buy some.

Narrator 3:   As the governor approached, the brothers bowed down before him.

Narrator 4:   They didn't realize that he was their brother Joseph.

Narrator 5:   Joseph recognized them, though.

Narrator 1:   Joseph didn't speak directly to them. He spoke through an interpreter to make them think that he couldn't speak their language.

Interpreter: Where do you come from?

Brothers:	We are from the land of Canaan. We would like to buy some food, please.
Narrator 2:	Joseph remembered his boyhood dream in which his brothers had bowed before him.
Narrator 3:	Joseph realized that his dream had come true. Joseph told his interpreter what to say next.
Joseph:	Tell them that I think they are spies. Make sure you sound angry.
Interpreter:	You are spies! You've come to see if our land is unprotected. You want to steal our grain!
Brothers:	No, my lord.
Simeon:	We have come only to buy food.
Reuben:	We are the sons of one man. We are honest men—not spies.
Judah:	Our father had 12 sons. One is dead, and the other remains with our father.
Narrator 4:	Joseph turned to his interpreter again. He told him what to say. (Joseph whispers to the interpreter.)
Interpreter:	If you want to prove that you are not spies, you will not leave this place until your younger brother arrives. One of you may leave to get your brother. But the rest of you will be put in prison.
Narrator 5:	Joseph's command was carried out. The 10 brothers were put in prison.
Narrator 1:	After three days, Joseph had his brothers sent to him.
Narrator 2:	Again Joseph told his interpreter what to say.
Interpreter:	Most of you may return home with grain to feed your families. But one of you must remain with me until the rest of you return with your youngest brother.
Narrator 3:	The brothers did not know that Joseph could understand them, so they talked freely among themselves.
Simeon:	We are being punished for what we did to Joseph.
Judah:	We ignored him when he pleaded with us. That is why we are being punished!
Reuben:	Didn't I tell you not to harm Joseph? You should have listened!
Narrator 4:	Joseph heard them and began to cry. He turned away so they would not see his tears.
Narrator 5:	Joseph had his brother Simeon tied up and taken to prison.

Narrator 1:	Joseph then ordered his brothers' bags to be filled with grain.
Narrator 2:	He also returned their silver coins to them. The coins were put on the top of the sacks before they were tied shut.
Narrator 3:	The brothers loaded their donkeys with the grain and left for Canaan, leaving Simeon behind in prison.
Narrator 4:	That night they stopped to eat and to feed their donkeys.
Dan:	Look what I found! The silver I paid for the grain is on the top of my sack.
Asher:	So is mine.
Reuben:	Now what has God done to us?
Narrator 5:	They returned home to Canaan and told Jacob what had happened.
Narrator 1:	They told Jacob that they could not return unless Benjamin went along.
Narrator 2:	Each of the brothers opened his sack and found that his money had been returned.
Narrator 3:	When they saw the money, they were afraid.
Narrator 4:	Jacob was scared and spoke angrily to his sons.
Jacob:	First I lost Joseph, and now Simeon. You will not take Benjamin with you to Egypt.
Reuben:	You may kill both of my sons if I do not bring Benjamin back to you. Trust me, Father. I will take care of Benjamin like he was my own son.
Jacob:	No! You will not take him. His brother is dead, and he is all that I have left of Rachel. If he is harmed, I won't be able to live.
Narrator 5:	The brothers left their father and returned to their families.

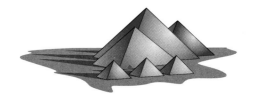

Joseph's Story

JOSEPH GAME CARDS: Mount the sheet on construction paper. Cut out the game cards. Practice putting them in order and telling the story of Joseph.

CUT

Joseph is born to Jacob and Rachel.	Jacob gives Joseph a beautiful coat.	Joseph dreams that 11 bundles of grain bow down to him.	Joseph dreams that the sun, moon, and stars bow down to him.
Jacob sends Joseph to check on his brothers and their flocks.	Joseph's brothers drag him into a cistern and sell him as a slave.	Joseph becomes a slave for Potiphar in Egypt.	Joseph is thrown into prison because of a lie told by Potiphar's wife.
Joseph tells the royal cupbearer what his dream about three grapevines means.	Joseph tells the royal baker what his dream about the three baskets of bread means.	Pharaoh has two dreams, about cows and ears of corn that come in sevens.	Joseph tells Pharaoh that seven good years will be followed by seven bad years of famine.
Pharaoh puts Joseph in charge of saving grain in Egypt during the seven good years.	Joseph's brothers come to Egypt for grain during the famine.	Joseph recognizes the brothers as they bow down to him.	Joseph keeps Simeon and sends the others back to get Benjamin.
Jacob finally lets the brothers take Benjamin to Egypt so that they can get more grain.	Joseph forgives his brothers after they try to protect Benjamin when the cup is found in his sack.	The brothers are afraid when Joseph tells them who he is.	Jacob and all his family move to Egypt.

The Brothers' Second Trip to Egypt

Imagine that a new children's book is coming out retelling the story of Joseph and his brothers. You have been asked to design the book cover and to write a title for the book. Design your book cover below. Don't forget to include the title in your design.

CUT

Reunion

Look at the four map locations. Write down what happened to Jacob a[nd his] family in each location. You may need to look up the Bible passages to [refresh] your memory.

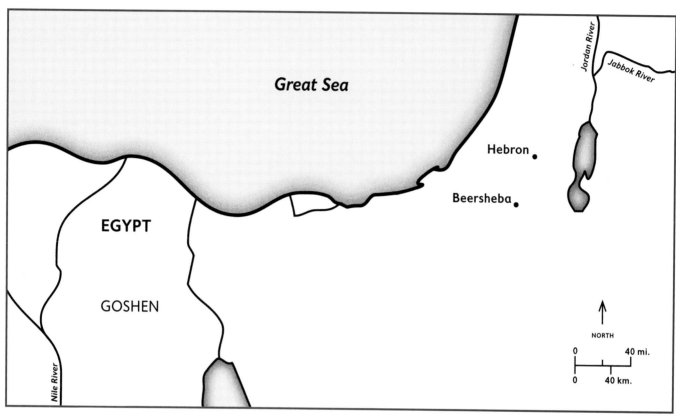

1. Hebron (Genesis 45:25–28) _____

   _____

2. Beersheba (Genesis 46:1–7) _____

   _____

   _____

   _____

3. Caravan trail to Egypt (Genesis 46:8–27) _____

   _____

4. Goshen (Genesis 46:28—47:12) _____

   _____

   _____

Family Tree

Use names from the word bank to fill in the blanks in the paragraph below. On the family tree put the name that has the same number as the number of the blank.

God called _____ (1) to leave Ur and go to a place he would show him. Abraham was 100 years old and his wife _____ (2) was 90 when their promised son was born. God told Abraham to sacrifice _____ (3). Abraham's servant went to Haran to get a wife for Isaac. Her name was _____ (4). Isaac and Rebekah had twin sons named Esau and _____ (5). Jacob went to Haran where he married _____ (6) and _____ (7). Jacob had 12 sons. _____ (8) was his favorite. _____ (9) was the youngest son. Kings would come from _____ (10). The other sons' names were _____ _____ (11–19). Jacob adopted Joseph's sons, _____ (20) and _____ (21), as his own sons before he died.

Word Bank	
Abraham	Leah
Asher	Levi
Benjamin	Manasseh
Dan	Naphtali
Ephraim	Rachel
Gad	Rebekah
Isaac	Reuben
Issachar	Sarah
Jacob	Simeon
Joseph	Zebulun
Judah	

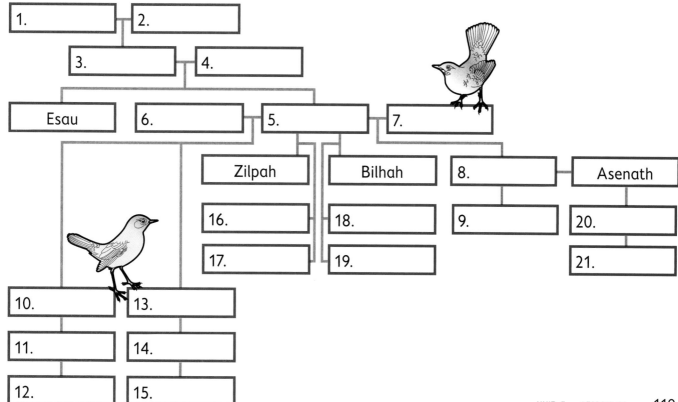

| 1. | 2. |
| 3. | 4. |

| Esau | 6. | 5. | 7. |

Zilpah	Bilhah	8.	Asenath
16.	18.	9.	20.
17.	19.		21.

10.	13.
11.	14.
12.	15.

Exodus 1:1–22
Before Moses

After reading the story, use the words below to fill in the [   ].

Jacob and his [   ] sons went to Egypt to join Joseph. After they all died,

the Israelites became very numerous. A new [   ] came to power. He was

afraid of the Israelites, so he made them [   ]. They were forced to make

[   ] and mortar. The king told the Hebrew [   ] to kill all of

the baby [   ], but they didn't do it. So Pharaoh gave this order to all

his [   ]: "Every boy that is born you must throw into the [   ],

but let every girl live."

Pharaoh	boys	bricks	people
slaves	Nile	eleven	midwives

Darkness

9

Death of firstborn son

10

The Plagues

FOLD

Why did God send the plagues?

1. _____

_____

2. _____

_____

3. _____

_____

4. _____

_____

Hail

7

Locusts

8

2

frogs

1

Nile River turns to blood

FOLD

Cattle die

5

Boils

6

FOLD

Gnats

3

Flies

4

The Passover

Match each phrase to **why** it is important. Write the letter on the line in front of the number.

_____ 1. Sacrifice the lamb.

_____ 2. Eat unleavened bread.

_____ 3. Eat bitter herbs.

_____ 4. Put blood on the doorframe.

_____ 5. Wear traveling clothes.

_____ 6. Celebrate Passover every year.

a. Reminder that God "passed over" Israelite homes.

b. Reminder of the journey out of Egypt.

c. Substitute for Israelite's firstborn son.

d. Reminder that they left Egypt in a hurry and did not have time to let the yeast work in the dough to make it rise.

e. Reminder of all God has done for his people.

f. Reminder of hard slavery in Egypt.

Answer each question below.

7. What did Jesus "pass over" for us? _____

_____

8. What do churches celebrate today instead of Passover? _____

_____

Imagine that you are getting ready to leave Egypt and are celebrating the first Passover feast. Use a paintbrush or crayon to show what your father does to the door.

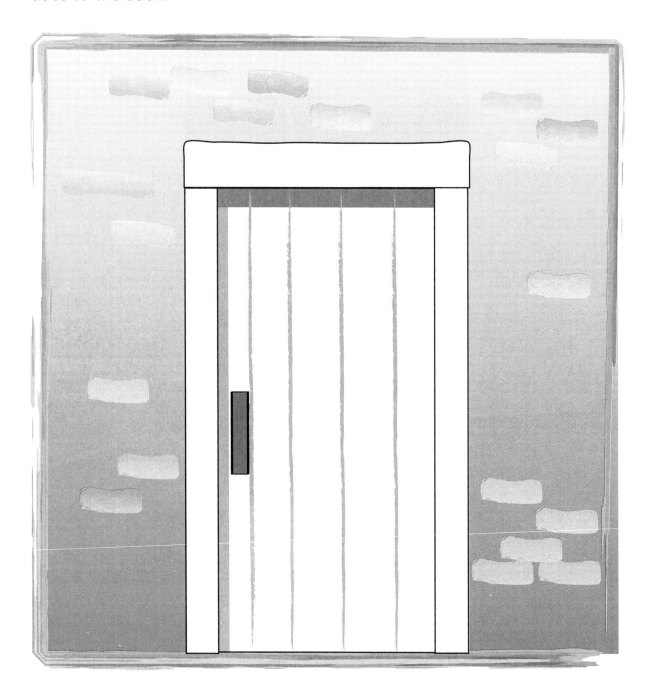

The Exodus

John: Yesterday was the most incredible day in our lives.

Erica: You'll be surprised to hear what happened to us yesterday.

Anna: Actually, you'll be surprised to hear what has been happening to us for the last year.

Abner: We're Israelites, but we've lived in Egypt with our families all of our lives.

Mark: The Egyptians don't like us very much.

Jessica: Our parents were slaves to the Egyptians. So were we.

Ethan: Every day we had to go out and help our parents make bricks under the hot Egyptian sun.

Deborah: We gathered straw to help our parents, and we brought them water and food.

Eunice: But all that changed when Moses came around.

Daniel: Our God told Moses to tell Pharaoh to let us go to worship our God.

Erica: When Pharaoh didn't agree, some pretty unbelievable things happened.

Abner: Those things were called plagues. The first three plagues hurt both the Egyptians and us.

Jessica: After that God sent the plagues only to the Egyptians.

Deborah: These plagues seemed like nothing compared with what God did for us yesterday.

Daniel: After the tenth plague, Pharaoh agreed to let us go.

John: He took one look at his dead child and couldn't get us out of Egypt fast enough.

Anna:	But it didn't take him too long to change his mind.
Mark:	It sure didn't! He must have started thinking about all of the work that wasn't going to get done if we weren't there to do it.
Ethan:	Pharaoh gathered his army and started to chase us.
Eunice:	We were camping at the edge of the sea for the night.
Daniel:	God was with us. He went before us in a cloud during the day and in a pillar of fire at night.
Erica:	The pillar of fire was incredible. We couldn't see the top of it. It gave off a glowing light as we got ready for bed.
John:	As we said before, it didn't take Pharaoh too long to miss us. I think he also wanted back all the gold and silver the Egyptians had given to us before we left.
Abner:	At first we didn't realize that Pharaoh's army was coming.
Jessica:	Most of us thought that the noise we heard was thunder.
Mark:	Then some of the people noticed that Pharaoh's army was charging straight at us.
Anna:	At first everybody was angry with Moses.
Daniel:	We couldn't believe that he'd led us into this trap.
Eunice:	Moses kept telling us about our powerful God, but our God didn't seem so powerful at that moment.
Ethan:	Moses told us not to be afraid. He said that God was taking care of us and that nothing bad was going to happen.
Deborah:	He even told us that we would never see the Egyptians again.
Ethan:	As Moses spoke to us, he stretched out his arm over the water.
Jessica:	A strong wind blew in from the east.
Abner:	While this was happening, the cloudy pillar, which had always been ahead of us, moved between us and the Egyptians.
Erica:	God was protecting us from the Egyptians. They could not see to get through the cloudy pillar.
Jessica:	What a fabulous sight we woke up to!

Water from a Rock

Use your Bible to complete the puzzle. When you're done, the column in the middle will tell where the story took place.

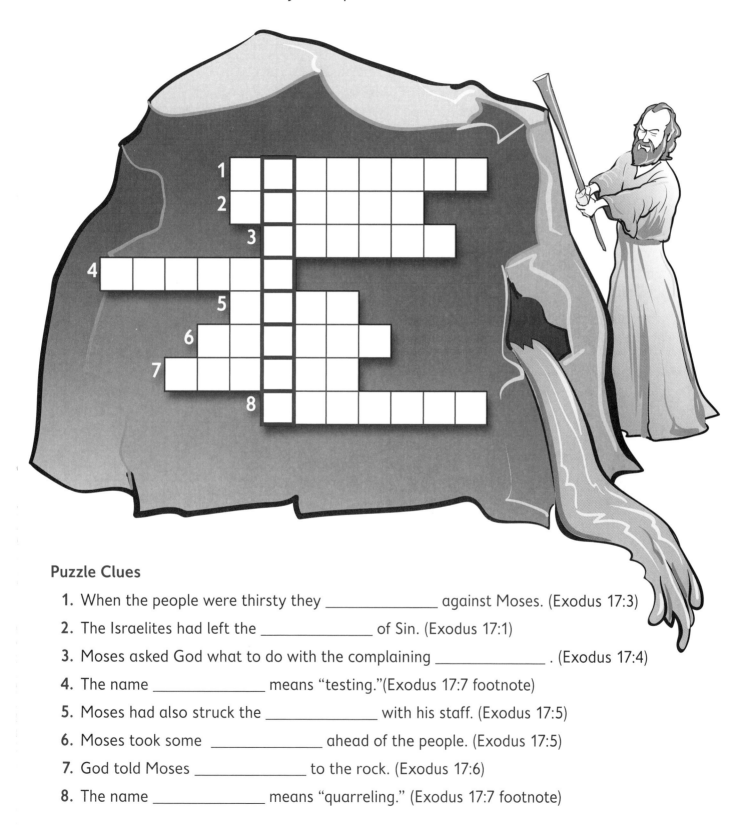

Puzzle Clues

1. When the people were thirsty they _____ against Moses. (Exodus 17:3)

2. The Israelites had left the _____ of Sin. (Exodus 17:1)

3. Moses asked God what to do with the complaining _____ . (Exodus 17:4)

4. The name _____ means "testing." (Exodus 17:7 footnote)

5. Moses had also struck the _____ with his staff. (Exodus 17:5)

6. Moses took some _____ ahead of the people. (Exodus 17:5)

7. God told Moses _____ to the rock. (Exodus 17:6)

8. The name _____ means "quarreling." (Exodus 17:7 footnote)

The Amalekites

Read the verses from Exodus 17. Fill in the blanks on the scroll. Illustrate each sentence.

Exodus 17:8–9

When the _____ attacked, Moses had the _____ of God in his hands.

Exodus 17:10–11

While _____ fought, _____ and _____ held up Moses' _____ so the Israelites would keep winning.

Exodus 17:12–13

They put a _____ under Moses, and Joshua overcame the Amalekites with the _____ .

Exodus 17:14–15

God told Moses to write it on a _____ . Then Moses built an _____ called the Lord is my _____ .

Bonus: How long did Moses' hands stay raised?

Love God above All

The Ten Commandments were not just a good set of rules for the people of Israel. They remain today as a set of guidelines for how we should live. Jesus also talked about the Ten Commandments. Read through each commandment, and then look up the New Testament passage. Write down a summary of what the verse or verses say.

Commandment	Passage
1. You shall have no other gods before me.	Matthew 10:37
2. You shall not make for yourself an idol.	Luke 16:13
3. You shall not misuse the name of the Lord your God.	Matthew 5:34–37
4. Remember the Sabbath day by keeping it holy.	Mark 2:27–28

1. Why do you think Jesus referred to these commandments as he taught his disciples?

_____

_____

_____

_____

_____

_____

2. How do Jesus' words help you to better understand the Ten Commandments?

_____

_____

_____

_____

_____

Love God above All

God gave people the Ten Commandments so that they would know how God wanted them to live. The first four commandments tell us that we should love God above all other things.

Write the number of the commandment that applies to each sentence below.

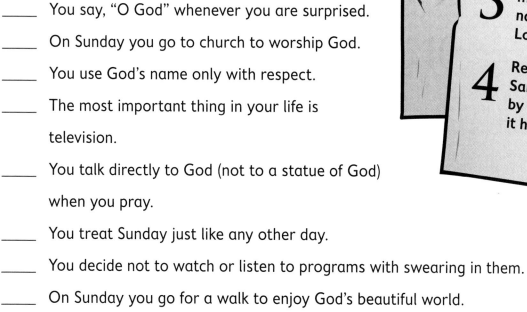

_____ You say, "O God" whenever you are surprised.

_____ On Sunday you go to church to worship God.

_____ You use God's name only with respect.

_____ The most important thing in your life is television.

_____ You talk directly to God (not to a statue of God) when you pray.

_____ You treat Sunday just like any other day.

_____ You decide not to watch or listen to programs with swearing in them.

_____ On Sunday you go for a walk to enjoy God's beautiful world.

Go back through the list, and draw a line through the situations that do not obey God's law.

Love Your Neighbor

Name _____

Jesus told his disciples how they were to treat others. Look up the Scripture passages that record Jesus' directions to his disciples. Write out or summarize each verse, and then answer the questions at the end of the activity sheet.

Commandment	Passage
5. Honor your father and your mother.	Luke 6:31 Matthew 10:37
6. You shall not murder.	Matthew 5:22
7. You shall not commit adultery.	Matthew 5:28
8. You shall not steal.	Luke 6:35
9. You shall not give false testimony against your neighbor.	Matthew 12:36–37
10. You shall not covet.	Luke 12:15

1. How can Jesus' words help you as you try to follow him and be kind to others?

_____

_____

_____

_____

_____

2. How would the world change if everyone obeyed these six commandments?

_____

_____

_____

_____

_____

Love Your Neighbor

In the first four commandments we are told to love God above everything else. The last six commandments tell us to love our neighbor as much as we love ourselves.

Write the number of the commandment that applies to each sentence below.

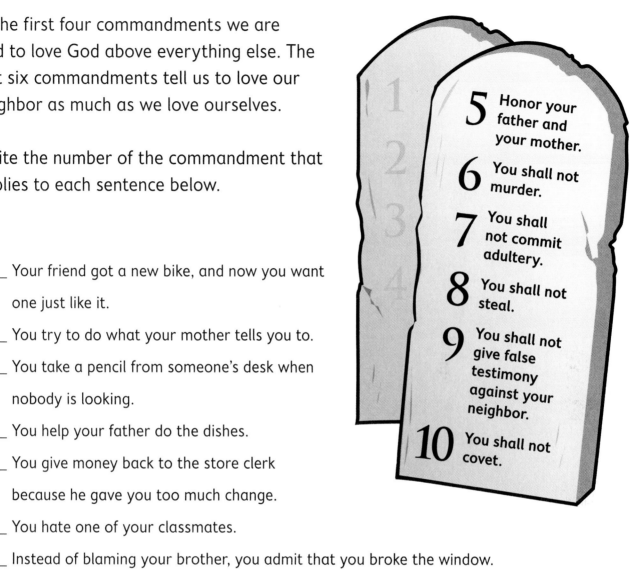

5 Honor your father and your mother.

6 You shall not murder.

7 You shall not commit adultery.

8 You shall not steal.

9 You shall not give false testimony against your neighbor.

10 You shall not covet.

_____ Your friend got a new bike, and now you want one just like it.

_____ You try to do what your mother tells you to.

_____ You take a pencil from someone's desk when nobody is looking.

_____ You help your father do the dishes.

_____ You give money back to the store clerk because he gave you too much change.

_____ You hate one of your classmates.

_____ Instead of blaming your brother, you admit that you broke the window.

_____ When you grow up, you are in love with your husband or wife and not in love with any other man or woman.

Go back through the list and draw a line through the situations that do not obey God's law.

Narrator 4:	Moses didn't want to see God destroy the Israelites, so Moses turned to God and said,
Moses:	Please don't destroy them, Lord. Remember how you brought them out of Egypt? What would the other nations say if you destroyed them? Please, Lord, remember your covenant with Abraham, Isaac, and Jacob. For the sake of these people, please don't destroy Israel.
Narrator 1:	God heard Moses' pleas and decided not to destroy the Israelites. God decided to punish them in another way.
Narrator 2:	As Moses came down the mountain, he met Joshua.
Narrator 3:	Joshua had come with Moses partway up the mountain and was waiting there for him to return.
Joshua:	Moses, the people are yelling and shouting. Do you think that they're all right? I hope there's not a war in the camp!
Moses:	Yes, Joshua, there is a war in the camp. But the people are not fighting a war against their enemies. They are fighting against God's commands.
Joshua:	What do you mean? God just gave them the Ten Commandments. Do you think they're disobeying them already?
Moses:	Yes. God told me so himself.
Narrator 4:	Moses grew more angry at the people of Israel with each step that he took.
Narrator 1:	When Moses saw the calf and the dancing, he threw the tablets with God's Law down the mountain.
Narrator 2:	The broken tablets landed at the foot of the mountain where the people had earlier stood to hear the Ten Commandments.
Narrator 3:	God had promised to be their God and that Israel would be his people.
Narrator 4:	The people had promised to serve only God and to obey him.
Narrator 1:	God had kept his promise, but his people had not kept theirs.
Narrator 4:	The covenant had been broken, just like the tablets.

Our Golden Calves

The Israelites put their own fears and a golden calf ahead of God. What things do we sometimes put ahead of God? Write examples of or draw pictures of these things on the pedestals below.

Holy and Pleasing

The Israelites had to follow many rules to be found holy in God's eyes. Jesus brought us salvation, and because we are thankful we must live lives that please him. Think of specific ways that you can live a life that is holy and pleasing to God.

Israel's Feasts

Your teacher will assign you one of the Scripture passages below. Look up the passage and fill in the chart. You will fill in the rest of the chart later, when other students present their passages.

Passage	Name of the Feast	When was it held?	Briefly describe the feast.
1. Exodus 12:1–14; Numbers 9:1–4			
2. Leviticus 23:15–22			

Passage	Name of the Feast	When was it held?	Briefly describe the feast.
3. Leviticus 16:29–34; Numbers 29:7–11			
4. Leviticus 23:33–43			
5. Leviticus 25:8–17, 54–55			

A Year at Mount Sinai

The year the Israelites spent at Mount Sinai was anything but dull. Finish each sentence with examples of events that happened while the Israelites were at Mount Sinai.

1. The best thing that happened was _____

_____

_____

2. The worst thing that happened was _____

_____

_____

3. The loudest time was _____

_____

4. The quietest time was _____

_____

_____

5. The event with the most color was _____

_____

6. The darkest event was _____

_____

7. The best choice a person made was _____

_____

8. The worst choice a person made was _____

_____

Spies Search the Land

Narrator 1: The Israelites sent out 12 spies to explore the land of Canaan. One spy was sent from each of the 12 tribes.

Narrator 2: The spies were leaders in their tribes. They had helped Moses in leading the people.

Narrator 3: These 12 spies were to report what they had seen to the Israelites. The people of Israel eagerly waited for them to return. They couldn't wait to hear the news.

Narrator 1: The spies explored Canaan for 40 days. When they came back, the people gathered to hear their report.

Spy 1: People of Israel and Moses, we are gathered here today to tell you what we found in the land of Canaan.

Spy 2: Canaan really is a land flowing with milk and honey.

Spy 3: Do you see what those two spies are carrying between them? It's a cluster of grapes!

Spy 4: As you can see, the cluster is too large for one man to carry alone.

Spy 5: It's even heavy for two of us to carry!

Joshua: This is just the beginning of what God has planned for us. All kinds of fruits grow in the land. They are large and sweet and waiting for us to pick them!

Spy 6: Joshua's getting a little bit carried away. He's right about the fruit, but he forgot to mention that the people who live in the land are huge—and strong.

Spy 7: There are many cities in Canaan, and each one is surrounded by tall, thick walls.

Caleb: Let's go right away and take the land. I saw nothing that can stop us.

Spy 2: Are you crazy? If we do that, we'll all die!

Spy 8: Their soldiers have much better weapons than we have.

Spy 9: We even saw the giants of Anak in the land.

Spy 10: We looked like grasshoppers next to them.

Spy 1: I refuse to go in and fight them right now, if ever.

Spy 3: We at least need time to get ready to fight.

Spy 5: It will take years for us to prepare to go to battle with the people we saw. We may never be ready to fight them.

Korah, Dathan, and Abiram

Name _____

Fill in the blanks, and then find the words in the word search.

L	V	D	Z	L	G	Y	X	U	M	Q	P	S	V	M
O	E	A	S	F	D	B	K	X	R	H	T	T	A	Q
R	I	Q	A	W	A	B	J	O	W	N	L	R	O	H
D	C	O	F	R	A	R	I	N	E	N	I	C	H	Q
J	O	S	A	R	O	L	E	T	N	B	B	K	M	F
P	Y	H	Y	Z	B	N	L	W	A	G	K	S	F	H
B	S	L	B	F	N	F	O	O	O	S	Y	D	T	J
X	M	G	D	Q	Q	D	U	M	W	H	A	N	Y	L
O	O	J	B	L	E	S	G	F	E	E	H	O	T	G
I	F	K	J	C	R	H	K	E	I	E	D	U	M	C
B	W	E	A	E	N	I	Q	D	O	R	T	T	P	L
T	V	F	S	B	F	C	V	R	Q	R	E	I	T	Z
W	A	N	B	B	I	A	Y	W	W	Z	Y	W	N	F
D	E	V	F	C	U	R	A	M	E	A	F	D	P	G
C	Z	U	E	J	B	Y	D	S	X	S	H	O	L	Y

1. Korah, Dathan, and _____ complained against Moses and Aaron. (Numbers 16:1)

2. These three men were joined by 250 others. They told Moses and Aaron that the entire Israelite community was _____ . (Numbers 16:3)

3. When Moses heard what they said, he fell _____ . (Numbers 16:4)

4. Moses proposed that Korah and his followers, along with Moses and Aaron, would take _____ with incense before the Lord the next morning. (Numbers 16:6)

5. Moses told Korah and his followers that they were grumbling against the _____ and not Aaron. (Numbers 16:11)

6. Moses, Aaron, and Korah and his followers gathered the next morning at the entrance to the Tent of _____ . (Numbers 16:18)

7. Moses warned the people to move back from the _____ of Korah, Dathan, and Abiram. (Numbers 16:26)

8. Korah, Dathan, Abiram, and all their families died when the earth _____ them up. (Numbers 16:32)

9. God sent _____ to destroy the 250 men who had followed the three men. (Numbers 16:35)

10. God told the people that no one except a descendant of _____ was to offer incense before the Lord. (Numbers 16:40)

Gifts from God

Think about gifts God has given you. Write one gift in each box.
Then decorate the boxes to look like presents.

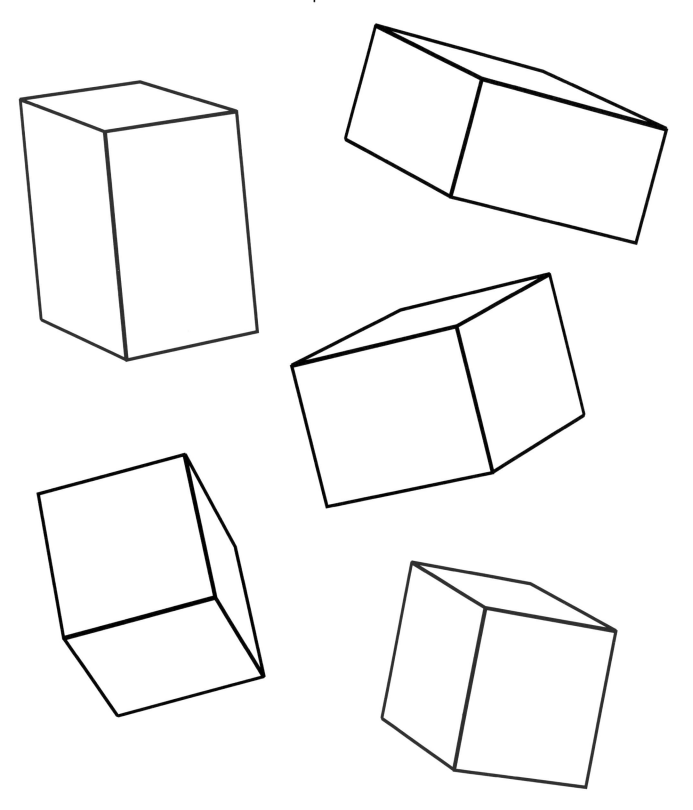

Numbers 20:2–13

Write a summary of the verses.

Draw a picture of what happened.

C U T

Numbers 20:1

Answer the questions.

who _____

what _____

when _____

where _____

Numbers 20:22–29

Fill in the blanks to complete the story.

The _____ spoke to Moses and Aaron

at Mount _____ . God said that _____

would not enter the land because he and Moses had

disobeyed at the waters of _____ . God told

Moses to take Aaron and his son _____ up

_____ Hor. Moses put Aaron's

on Eleazar. _____ died on top of the

mountain. When the Israelites found out that Aaron

had died, they mourned for _____ days.

CUT

Numbers 20:14–21

Answer the questions.

What request did Moses send to the King of Edom?

What answer did he send to Moses?

What finally happened?

Questions, Please

Name _____

Write questions for the following answers in the four categories on activity sheet b. Add up your points for each correct question when you are finished (100 points = first row, 200 points = second row, 300 points = third row, 400 points = fourth row).

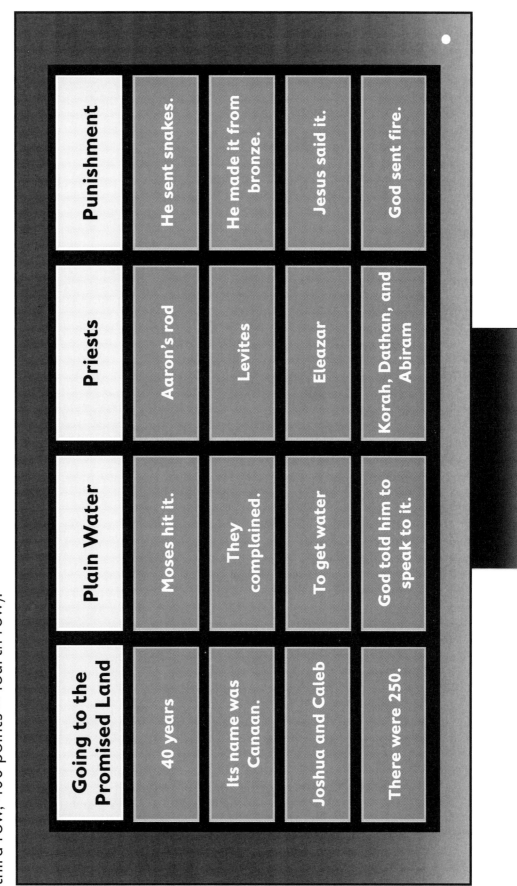

Going to the Promised Land	Plain Water	Priests	Punishment
40 years	Moses hit it.	Aaron's rod	He sent snakes.
Its name was Canaan.	They complained.	Levites	He made it from bronze.
Joshua and Caleb	To get water	Eleazar	Jesus said it.
There were 250.	God told him to speak to it.	Korah, Dathan, and Abiram	God sent fire.

Name _____

Going to the Promised Land	Plain Water	Priests	Punishment
Going to the Promised Land	Plain Water	Priests	Punishment
Going to the Promised Land	Plain Water	Priests	Punishment
Going to the Promised Land	Plain Water	Priests	Punishment

Balaam and His Donkey

Narrator 1: Early one morning Balaam got up and prepared to go with the princes from Moab.

Narrator 2: He saddled his donkey and started down the road toward Moab.

Voice of God: You may go with the visitors only if you speak the words I give you.

Narrator 3: God knew that Balaam was going with the men because they had promised him money.

Narrator 4: Balaam planned to speak his own words so that Balak would be happy with him and pay him well.

Narrator 5: Balaam rode his donkey down the road, thinking about what he would say to Balak.

Narrator 6: Suddenly Balaam's donkey left the road and turned into a field.

Narrator 1: Balaam began to whip his donkey, trying to get her back on the road.

Narrator 2: Balaam did not know that the donkey had stepped off the road because she had seen an angel with a drawn sword.

Narrator 3: Balaam's donkey returned to the road. She walked on a narrow path between two vineyards.

Narrator 4: Walls had been built on both sides of the path.

Narrator 5: Once again an angel of the Lord appeared before the donkey. Balaam could not see the angel, but the donkey could.

Narrator 6: The donkey was terrified and tried to get as far away from the angel as she could.

Narrator 1: Balaam's leg was crushed between the wall and his donkey.

Narrator 2:	Balaam beat his donkey. He wanted her to move so that his foot could be freed.
Narrator 3:	The angel again moved ahead of the donkey and blocked her path.
Narrator 4:	The donkey saw that there was no place for her to go. She lay down, pinning Balaam underneath.
Narrator 5:	Balaam could not believe that his donkey could be so stubborn and useless.
Narrator 6:	He began to beat the donkey again.
Narrator 1:	God opened the mouth of Balaam's donkey.
Donkey:	What have I done, master, to make you beat me three times?
Balaam:	You have made a fool of me! If I had a sword in my hand, I would kill you right now.
Donkey:	Am I not your own donkey that has given you rides for many years? Have I ever treated you the way I did today?
Balaam:	No. You haven't.
Narrator 2:	Balaam didn't seem to notice how odd it was to speak with his donkey.
Narrator 3:	Then God opened Balaam's eyes, and he saw the angel of the Lord standing in the road with his sword drawn.
Narrator 4:	Balaam fell facedown before the angel.
Angel:	Why have you beaten your donkey three times? I am here to stop you from foolishly following your own will rather than God's. The donkey saw me and turned away from me. She protected you from my sword. If she had not turned away, you would have died.
Balaam:	I have sinned against God. I did not see you standing in the road. If you want, I'll go back to my house and not go to Moab.
Angel:	You may go to Moab, but you are to say only what God tells you.
Narrator 5:	Balaam mounted his donkey again and traveled to Balak, King of Moab.
Balak:	What took you so long, Balaam? I told you to hurry.
Balaam:	Well, I'm here now. But I can say only what God puts in my mouth.
Balak:	Tomorrow I will take you to a high hill where you can see the people of Israel. We'll offer sacrifices and hear what God says to you.

Narrator 6:	The next morning Balaam ordered that seven altars be prepared and animals sacrificed on them.
Narrator 1:	Balaam walked away from Balak and the sacrifices. He could see the many people of Israel camped in the distance.
Narrator 2:	Balaam returned to Balak and said what God had told him.
Balaam:	How can I curse the people God has blessed? I see before me the many people of Israel. Who can count their vast numbers?
Balak:	What have you done to me? I brought you here to curse my enemies! You just blessed the people I want to destroy!
Balaam:	I'm sorry, but I can speak only what God tells me.
Balak:	Well, I'm taking you to another place. Let's see if you have something different to say there.
Narrator 3:	Balak took Balaam to the top of Pisgah and built seven more altars.
Narrator 4:	More animals were sacrificed while Balaam walked away to hear what God had to say to him.
Narrator 5:	When Balaam returned, Balak asked what God had told him.
Balaam:	The Lord God is with the people of Israel. He brought them out of Egypt and will keep them from harm. They have the strength of the wild ox.
Balak:	This is worse than the first time. Please stop blessing them!
Balaam:	I told you that I must do what the Lord says.
Balak:	Well, let's try again. I'm going to take you to another place. This will be closer to the people of Israel. Maybe if you can see them more clearly, you'll have a different message from God.
Narrator 6:	Once again seven altars were built and animals sacrificed.
Narrator 1:	Balaam looked out over the tribes of Israel, and God's Spirit came upon him.
Balaam:	How beautiful are your tents, O Jacob, your dwelling places, O Israel! May those who bless you be blessed and those who curse you be cursed!
Balak:	What are you doing? I told you to curse my enemies. Instead you blessed them three times. Get out of here! I'm not going to pay you.
Narrator 2:	Balaam returned home. Balak tried to find another way to defeat the people of Israel.

Balaam in the New Testament

Read the Scripture passages and fill in the chart below.

Scripture	Summary of the Passage	Message to God's People
2 Peter 2:1–3, 15–16		
Jude 3–4, 11		
Revelation 2:14–16		

Why do you think the New Testament writers used Balaam as an example? _____

God Defeats Balaam

Name _____

Number the sentences in the correct order. Do each set separately.

Set 1

_____ The angel of the Lord blocked Balaam's way.

_____ Balaam blessed the Israelites instead of cursing them.

_____ Balaam's donkey talked to him.

_____ Balak was afraid of the Israelite army because he knew that he couldn't defeat them.

_____ Balaam beat his donkey.

_____ Balak sent for Balaam and asked him to curse the Israelites.

_____ God opened Balaam's eyes so he could see the angel.

_____ Balaam went with the people Balak had sent.

_____ After defeating Sihon and Og, Israel camped by the Jordan.

Set 2

_____ All of the Midianite men were killed. The women, children, and animals were captured.

_____ God sent a plague that killed 24,000 Israelites.

_____ Balaam told the Midianites how to make God angry with the Israelites.

_____ The Israelites sacrificed to Baal.

_____ The Israelites defeated the Midianites and the Moabites.

WHY DIDN'T HE JUST LISTEN TO ME IN THE FIRST PLACE?

Cities of Refuge

Label each city of refuge on the map.

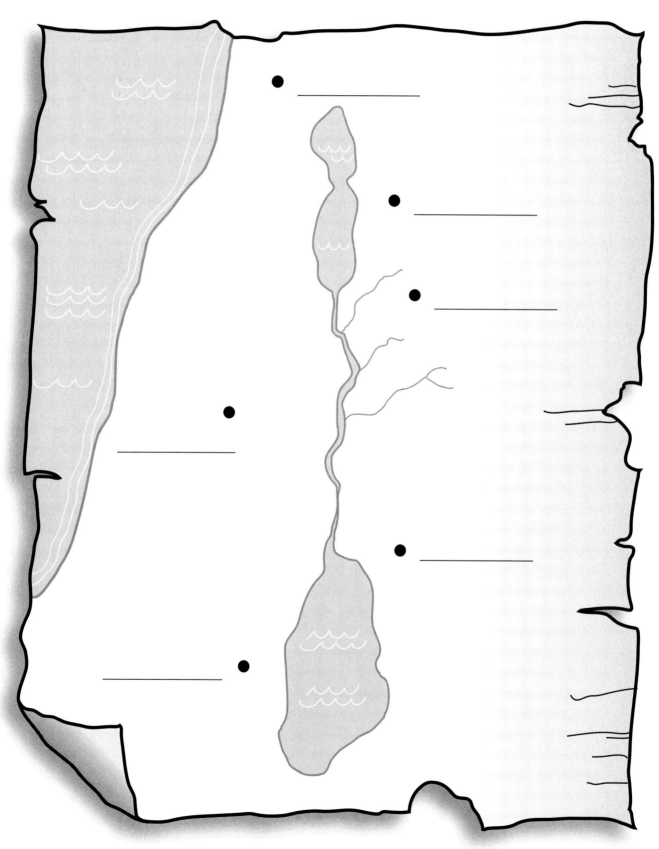

How Can I Help?

Imagine that you write an advice column for the Israelite newspaper *The Desert Daily.* How would you respond to the following letter in your column?

B4 MONDAY, 5 ZIV 1423 ▲ **THE DESERT DAILY**

NEW LEADER APPOINTED!

Letter requesting advice:

Dear Seth or Sarah,

A friend from my tribe has just been appointed to replace Moses as the leader of the Israelites. He is very nervous about his new responsibilities and about how to handle the grumbling and complaining that seem so common. How can I help him? What advice can I give?

—*Faithful Friend, Somewhere in the Desert*

Seth and Sarah

Dear Faithful Friend,

_____

_____

_____

_____

_____

_____

_____

_____

_____

Moses

Think about the life of Moses. God used him even though he wasn't perfect.

1. Make a list of things that made Moses less than perfect.

   _____

   _____

   _____

   _____

2. Write a short paragraph about how God used him anyway. Draw a picture of Moses accomplishing something for God.

3. On another sheet, draw a picture of YOU accomplishing something for God!

The Story of Rahab

Crossing the Red Sea and the Jordan River

	Crossing the Red Sea	Crossing the Jordan River
Who led the people of Israel?		
How did the water part?		
How did the water return to its natural course?		
What happened to the Israelites' enemies after the Israelites crossed?		

Mountain Poem

Choose either Achan or Joshua, and write a poem following the directions below.

1. Write the name *Joshua* or *Achan.*

2. Write down two words describing him.

3. Write down three words describing the setting of the story.

4. Write down four words describing the problem in the story.

5. Write down five words describing God's reaction

   to the problem.

6. Write down six words describing how the

   problem was solved.

7. Write down seven words telling what

   lesson the people of Israel learned.

8. Write down eight words telling

   what lesson you learned

   from the story.

Name _____

1

2

3

4

5

6

7

8

Achan and Ai

Fill in the blanks.

1 When Achan helped to destroy Jericho, he

took _____ .

2 When Achan got back to his tent, he

_____

_____ .

3 Joshua decided that the next city to attack

would be _____ . Joshua's scouts

found out that Ai had a small army, so

Joshua sent only _____ men.

4 What happened next? _____

_____

_____ .

5

God told Joshua that the Israelites had been

defeated because _____

_____ . Joshua called the leaders

together to tell them what God had said.

6

God pointed out that the guilty man was

_____ . As punishment he and his

family _____ .

7

The Lord gave Joshua a new plan. He told him

to hide 30,000 men behind _____ .

The next morning Joshua led some soldiers

against the soldiers of that city.

8

Joshua and his men lured the soldiers of Ai

into the desert. The hidden soldiers of Israel

_____ .

The victory belonged to God and his people.

Victory over the Southern Kings

1 Five Canaanite kings heard about Israel's victories and alliance with Gibeon. They decided to fight Gibeon. Gibeon sent this message to Israel: _____

_____

2 Joshua and his army caught the kings attacking Gibeon by surprise. The Canaanite kings fled from the Israelites but didn't get far because _____

_____ .

3 Joshua was afraid that the kings would get away during the night. But God _____

_____

_____ .

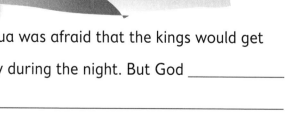

4 The Israelites trapped the five kings in a cave. Later Joshua _____ .
Joshua and his army pursued and destroyed the other soldiers before going back to Gilgal.

The Five Kings

Name _____

Across

1. Joshua and the people were camped at _____ when they received word that the Gibeonites were being attacked. (Joshua 10:6)

2. Adoni-Zedek was the king of _____ (Joshua 10:1)

4. Joshua and the Israelites conquered all these lands because the _____ was with them. (Joshua 10:42)

5. The kings were later killed and buried in the cave where they had been _____ . (Joshua 10:27)

7. Joshua and the people of Israel left no _____ in the cities that they conquered. (Joshua 10:30)

10. The five kings fled the battle and hid in a _____ . (Joshua 10:16)

12. God sent _____ , which fell on the heads of the Amorite soldiers as they ran from the Israelites. (Joshua 10:11)

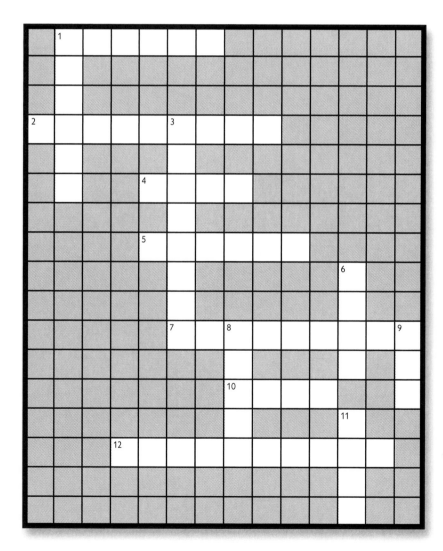

Down

1. Adoni-Zedek was worried because the people of _____ had made a treaty with the Israelites. (Joshua 10:1)

3. The five kings of the _____ joined together to fight Israel. (Joshua 10:5)

6. Joshua asked God to let the _____ stand still over the Valley of Aijalon. (Joshua 10:12)

8. Joshua had the people build a monument of _____ at the mouth of the cave. (Joshua 10:27)

9. Joshua asked God to let the _____ stand still over Gibeon. (Joshua 10:12)

11. Joshua's army commanders put their _____ on the necks of the kings to show the Israelites' complete victory. (Joshua 10:24)

The Conquest of Canaan

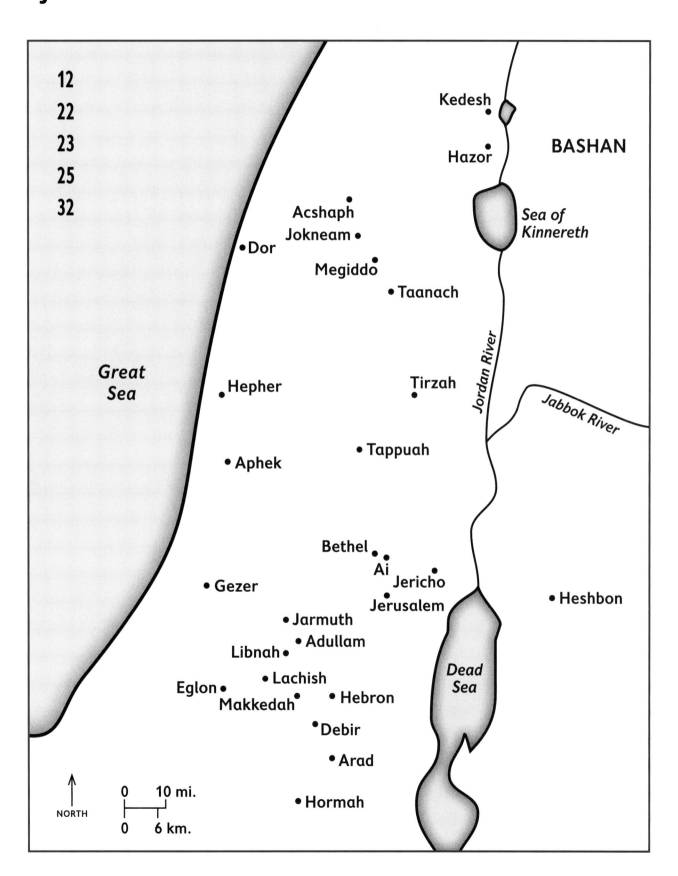

12
22
23
25
32

Great
Sea

Dor

Acshaph
Jokneam
Megiddo
Taanach

Hepher

Aphek

Tappuah

Tirzah

Bethel
Ai
Jericho
Jerusalem

Gezer

Jarmuth
Adullam

Libnah

Lachish

Eglon
Makkedah
Hebron

Debir

Arad

Hormah

Kedesh

Hazor

BASHAN

Sea of
Kinnereth

Jordan River

Jabbok River

Heshbon

Dead
Sea

NORTH

0   10 mi.

0   6 km.

The Conquest of Canaan

Name _____

Turn to Genesis 17:7–8. God made this promise to Abraham many years before the Israelites conquered Canaan. Fill in the boxes to complete the verse. Then use the numbers under the letters to fill out the sentence below.

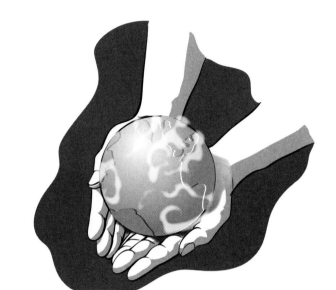

"I will _____ my covenant as an _____ _____ between me
and you and your _____ after you for the generations to _____,
to be your _____ and the God of your descendants after you. The _____
_____ of Canaan, where you are now an alien, I will give as an _____
possession to you and your _____ after you; and I will be their _____."

(Word boxes with numbered letters)

⬜⬜⬜ [K]⬜⬜⬜ ⬜⬜⬜ ⬜⬜⬜⬜⬜⬜⬜⬜⬜ ⬜⬜
8 6 7   1 14 5   11 4 9   14 12 6 2 4 9 1 9   5 6

⬜⬜⬜⬜⬜⬜⬜ ⬜⬜⬜ ⬜⬜ [K]⬜⬜⬜⬜ ⬜⬜⬜
3 15 12 3 11 3 2   3 13 7   11 1   1 1 14 9   11 4 9

⬜⬜⬜⬜⬜⬜⬜⬜⬜ ⬜⬜ ⬜⬜!
14 12 6 2 4 9 1 9   5 6   10 9

The Israelites Settle in the Land

Write the name of each tribe in the correct area.

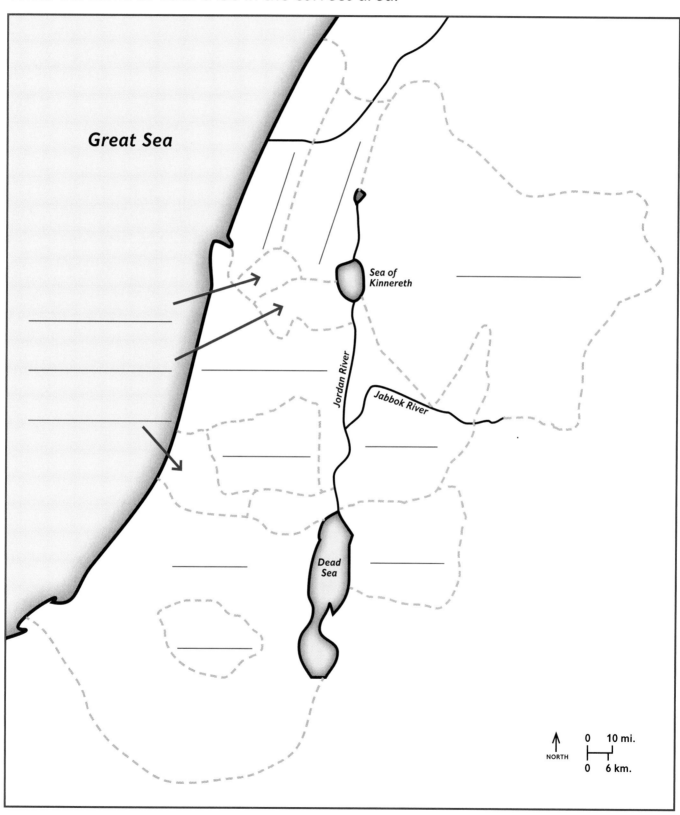

Great Sea

Sea of
Kinnereth

Jordan River

Jabbok River

Dead
Sea

NORTH

0   10 mi.

0   6 km.

Covenant Review

Name _____

Read each Bible passage. Write the name of the person with whom God made the covenant. In the box, draw a symbol of that covenant.

1. Genesis 9:12–17 _____

2. Genesis 15:1–6 _____

3. Exodus 34:4–14 _____

4. Joshua 24:14–27 _____

Bible Dictionary

ALTAR OF BURNT OFFERING

The altar of burnt offering (bronze altar), which had a horn at each corner, was carved from one piece of wood. The altar was covered with bronze. A horn was carved at each of the four corners from the same piece of wood, which was then covered with bronze. A bronze grate rested on a ledge halfway down on the inside of the altar. The altar was hollow so that it was light enough to carry. When the Israelites wandered in the desert, the priests carried the altar with poles slipped through four rings on its sides. When the Israelites set up the tabernacle, they filled the altar with sand and placed it in the tabernacle courtyard. The priests offered five kinds of sacrifices on this altar: the burnt offering, grain offering, fellowship offering, sin offering, and guilt offering.

BLESSING

A blessing in the Old Testament was a special promise made to a person. The blessing promised that the person would receive a special gift, often from God. A father passed on his property and his authority over the family to his son through a blessing. A father also used the blessing to give special instructions to his sons. He told his son all that would be his in the future if he lived according to his father's—and God's—commands. Blessings could turn into curses if the son did not obey the commands.

BRICKMAKING

Bricks were an important building material in ancient Egypt. The white or light red bricks were used in all buildings except for temples and palaces, which were made of stone. When the Israelites were slaves in Egypt, they made enough bricks to build royal cities for the pharaoh. The Israelites made the bricks by mixing mud from the Nile River with short pieces of straw. They mixed the straw and mud together with their feet. This mixture was pressed into molds and then baked

Bricks

in the sun until it was dry and hard. The straw kept the bricks from cracking or bending as they dried.

Another way of making bricks was shaping the bricks by hand. Hand-shaped bricks were oval and harder to stack.

CANAANITES

Canaan was the son of Ham, who was the son of Noah. The Canaanites were Ham's descendants. They lived in the land between Egypt and Syria. Because the soil was very rich, most Canaanites were farmers.

The Canaanites worshiped many gods. When Joshua led the Israelites into Canaan, the Israelites didn't completely destroy the Canaanites. Because the Canaanites lived among the Israelites, the Israelites began to worship the Canaanite gods. Baal and Ashtoreth were two Canaanite gods the Israelites sometimes worshiped.

CARAVANS

Travel in Bible times was dangerous because of the poor roads, robbers, and wild animals. People usually traveled in groups, which was safer. These traveling groups were called caravans. Poor people walked; rich people rode donkeys or camels.

Traders usually traveled in caravans. They used donkeys or camels to carry their goods. Some caravans had hundreds of camels. Each camel could carry a load weighing 500 pounds.

Many important trade routes passed through Canaan. Caravans carried goods from one country to another using these trade routes. Slaves, grain, spices, gold, silver, jewelry, medicines, cloth, and precious stones were some of these goods.

CHILDLESSNESS

During Bible times, children were considered a blessing from the Lord. Children, especially boys, carried on the family name. It was a disgrace not to have children. If a woman couldn't have a baby, some people made fun of her. A wife who didn't have children was thought to be less valuable than one who did. Wives with no children were thought to be cursed, and their husbands were allowed to divorce them.

CISTERNS

A cistern was a large covered tank dug into the rock under the ground.

Cistern

Drainage tunnels or troughs guided rainwater to the cistern, where it was stored. Cisterns were usually bottle-shaped and very deep—often over 100 feet (30 meters) deep. Each cistern had one or more openings for people to draw water from.

Palestine received very little rain during the summer, so it was very important for the people to save water during the rainy season (October–April). Many houses had their own cisterns, and cities had public cisterns so that enough water could be saved for everybody.

Sometimes empty cisterns were used as prisons. Joseph's brothers threw him into a cistern before they sold him. Jeremiah was thrown into a muddy cistern when the Israelites didn't like his prophecies.

CITIES

Cities in Canaan were started by nomads who decided to stay in one place and become farmers. Sometimes people who were still nomads stole the farmers' crops, so the farmers banded together and built cities to protect themselves. They built these cities near water and farmland. The people farmed their crops during the day and returned to the city at night.

The Canaanite cities had thick walls and a gate that was closed at night. A watchtower was often built next to the gate. From the tower watchmen could watch for danger. Inside the city was a

City walls and gate

tower or stronghold where the people could hide when an enemy attacked. Just inside the city gate was an open area where the people met together to make their business deals. Judges sat near the gate and decided cases there.

The city streets were narrow and winding. Often craftsmen and merchants set up shops on a certain street. This street was known as the market.

Each Canaanite city had its own king.

CITIES OF REFUGE

At the time the Israelites entered Canaan, the nearest male relative of a person who had been killed was required to take vengeance. This person was called the avenger.

The cities of refuge were to be a safe place for people who had accidentally killed someone. The accused person could run to the city before the slain person's relatives came to avenge their loved one's death. The leaders of the city would then hold a trial to decide whether the death was accidental or deliberate. More than one witness was required to testify at the trial so that the leaders of the city could determine the truth.

If the person was found to have committed murder, the family of the victim was allowed to have the murderer killed. An innocent person was set free, but he or she could be safe only inside the city of refuge. If he or she decided to leave, the family of the dead person could still seek vengeance. Only when the high priest of the city of refuge died could the accused return home. The high priest of each city was appointed for life, so some people never returned home.

Before the Israelites entered Canaan, Moses set up three cities of refuge east of the Jordan River. Joshua established three more cities of refuge west of the Jordan River when the land was divided. These cities were spread throughout Israel so people could get to one easily if necessary.

COVENANT

A covenant is an agreement between two groups or two people. In early Bible times covenants were made between great kings and less powerful kings. In these royal covenants the great king promised to do something for the weaker king—usually to protect him. The covenant also spelled out what the weaker king had to do for the great king. Often he had to pay taxes to the great king.

God's covenants with his people followed the form of the royal covenants of the time. God promised to protect and care for his people if they worshiped and obeyed him. Knowing that the people could not do this perfectly, God gave them rules for sacrifices. The sacrifices paid for the people's disobedience. God said that his covenant would last forever. He listed blessings for those who kept the covenant and curses for those who broke it.

In his covenant with Noah God promised to never again send a flood to destroy the Earth (Genesis 9:8–17). In his covenant with Abraham, Isaac, Jacob, and the Israelites God promised that he would be their God, promised them the land of Canaan, and promised to bless all nations of the Earth through Abraham. God later promised David that his descendants would rule forever (2 Samuel 7:5–16). Jesus, who was the descendant of Abraham and David, fulfilled all of these promises.

God made his covenant new in Jesus. Jesus paid for all of the sins that broke the covenant with God.

DESERT

Summer is very hot and dry in the area of Canaan. The Negev Desert is south of Canaan, and the huge Arabian Desert borders Canaan on two sides. During the winter, winds blowing across the Mediterranean Sea bring rain to Canaan but not to the desert areas further inland.

Desert land

The desert is not a lifeless place, however. The steppe, the land of the nomads, usually receives about 12 inches (30 cm) of rain during the winter season. After the winter rains, the steppe is covered with green plants and new grass for the herds. Small shrubs and other hardy plants grow in the low desert hills. These plants provide food for the sheep, goats, camels, and other animals.

Water from underground springs allows palm trees and grass to grow in certain small areas. Each of these areas is called an oasis.

DREAMS

One way that God spoke to people in Old Testament times was through dreams. God sent dreams during times of danger or to prepare people for coming events. The dreams God sent often contained images that stood for something else.

People who didn't believe in God saw dreams as a way for their gods to tell them about future events.

These people wanted to have dreams because they wanted to know about their futures. Some rulers had all of their dreams written down in a book. The meaning of each dream was also written down so they could look back later to see whether the dream had come true.

God gave both Joseph and Daniel the ability to interpret other people's dreams. They used this ability to help both their own people and foreigners. God sometimes used the dreams of others to help his chosen people.

God speaks to us today through his Word, the Bible. But our dreams can tell us things about ourselves, too. They can tell us if we're worried about something or if we're afraid of something. Most of our dreams reflect what happened to us during the day or what we were thinking about before we went to bed.

Jabbok river, the site of Jacob's dream

EDOMITES

The Edomites lived in Edom—a rugged region south of Moab and the

Dead Sea. Edom has lots of mountains. The land is made of red sandstone. The Edomites were "brothers" of Israel because they were descendants of Esau, Jacob's brother. The Edomites worshiped idols, not the one true God of the Israelites.

When Moses wanted to lead Israel through Edom on the way to Canaan, the Edomites wouldn't permit it. The Israelites didn't want to fight their "brothers," so they turned back and went around Edom. Many years later, King Saul and King David fought against Edom and partially defeated the Edomites. When the Babylonians captured Judah and forced the people to move to Babylon, the Edomites moved into Judah.

GARDEN OF EDEN

The word *Eden* means "pleasant."

A river flowed in the Garden of Eden. As it left the garden, it divided into four smaller rivers: the Pishon, the Gihon, the Tigris, and the Euphrates. Ancient maps show where the Tigris and Euphrates were, but the Pishon and Gihon cannot be located. When Adam and Eve sinned, God drove them out of the Garden of Eden.

GODS

The people who lived in Canaan and the surrounding areas worshiped many different gods. The people believed that separate gods ruled each part of nature and life and that sometimes these gods fought each other to see which one was the strongest.

Because they lived in Egypt for so long, the Israelites knew a lot about the gods the Egyptians worshiped. Some of the Israelites knew more about the Egyptian gods than they did about the Lord. When trouble came, the Israelites were tempted to worship the idol gods rather than trust the Lord.

Apis was the Egyptian bull god, the god of strength and power. He looked like a bull with a square spot on its forehead, an eagle-shaped spot on its back, and a beetle-shaped mark on its tongue. While the Israelites waited for Moses to return from Mount Sinai with the Ten Commandments, they asked Aaron to make an image like Apis. They remembered how the Egyptians had worshiped Apis to get strength.

Asherah statue

Asherah was a Canaanite mother goddess. Sometimes she was called the goddess of the sea. Poles with her image carved on them were placed in many cities and houses. When Jeroboam was king of Israel, he set up Asherah poles for the Israelites to worship.

Ashtoreth, Baal's female companion (see Baal, below), was the Canaanite goddess of love and war. She was also called Astarte or Ishtar.

Baal was the most important Canaanite god. His symbol was the bull. The Canaanites believed that Baal controlled storms, and they called him "he who rides on the clouds." Because storms brought life-giving rain, Baal was worshiped as the source of life. The Canaanites built many shrines and temples where they sacrificed to Baal. When they needed something very important, they even sacrificed their children on Baal's altar.

Dagon was the main Philistine god. He was the weather god who was thought to bring rain. Because rain made the crops grow, Dagon also became known as the grain god. The temple in Gaza was dedicated to Dagon.

Re (also spelled Ra) was the Egyptian sun god. The Egyptians had over 400 gods. They worshiped the Nile River as the source of life. They worshiped a ram god, a cow god, a frog god, a cat god, a god of the dead, a god of wisdom, and so on.

Because the Israelites had only one God, they were very different from their neighbors, who had dozens of gods. But the main difference between the Israelites and their neighbors was that the Israelites worshiped the true God, while their neighbors worshiped idols made of wood and stone. God commanded the Israelites not to worship any of their neighbors' idols. The Israelites were to worship only God and to worship him in spirit and in truth.

HIGH PRIEST

The covenant with God was broken by sin, so people could not talk directly to God. The people needed someone to talk to God for them and to tell them what God said. The high priest became the mediator between God and the Israelites. When the high priest stood before the people, he represented God; when he stood before God, he represented the people. The high priest's job also included offering sacrifices, and he was the only one ever allowed in the Most Holy Place.

God appointed the Levites to be Israel's priests. Aaron was the first high priest. Eleazar, Aaron's son, became the next high priest. Phinehas, Eleazar's son, became the next high priest. Eli was the high priest when Samuel was brought to the tabernacle.

Priests wore long, white linen tunics with long sleeves. When the high priest went into the Most Holy Place he put a long blue robe over his tunic. The robe had little golden bells and pomegranates (red fruit the size of an orange) made of colored linen cloth sewn onto the bottom. Over the robe the high priest put a red, blue, and purple ephod, which looked like an apron. The ephod was held together at the shoulders with onyx stones that had the names of the 12 tribes of Israel engraved on them. The high priest put on a breastpiece, which was tied to gold rings on the ephod with blue lacing. The breastpiece had 12 jewels, one for each tribe of Israel. The high priest tied a girdle (belt) around his waist. He covered his head with a turban that had a gold plate attached in front. The gold plate said "Holy to the Lord." This was a reminder that the high priest carried the sins of the people before the Lord.

Jesus became our high priest when he died on the cross. He took away our sins and is the mediator between God and us.

INHERITANCE

In Old Testament times a father's possessions were given to his sons when he died. Each son received some part of his father's possessions. The oldest son, however, was considered special. The oldest, or firstborn, son received twice as many possessions as the other sons. He also became the head of the household. People in Old Testament times wanted at least one son to carry on the family's name and work.

JEWELRY

In early Bible times jewelry was a sign of wealth. People used jewelry instead of money to trade and buy. When a man and woman got married, jewelry was given to the bride's family. When people won a battle, they took jewelry and other things from their enemies.

Gold, silver, bronze, and precious stones were made into earrings, neck-laces, bracelets, headbands, rings,

and belts. Stones called gems were set into the metal. One of these gems was onyx, which had black and white layers. When letters were carved into onyx, the white letters against the black were easy to see. Other gems used in jewelry were emeralds, sapphires, amethysts, and agates.

Jewelry was also used in worship. The high priest's breastpiece contained 12 gems, one for each tribe of Israel.

The Egyptians wore jewelry that they believed would keep evil away from them. When the Israelites left Egypt, the Egyptians gave them many pieces of gold and silver jewelry (Exodus 12:35–36). The Israelites used some of this jewelry to make the golden calf (Exodus 32:2). Later they gave a lot of their jewelry to God as gifts for the building of the tabernacle (Exodus 35:20–29).

MUSIC

Music was very important to the Israelites. The Israelites used their voices and instruments to make music. Music was a part of all important occasions: festivals, worship, and even funerals. The people of Israel became known by their neighbors as musicians. King David was probably the most famous Israelite musician.

The melodies the Israelites sang were very simple. They sounded more like chanting than singing. The lead singer or singers would sing one line, and the people would repeat it after them. The songwriters often put new words with old tunes.

The Israelites used three main types of instruments: stringed instruments, wind instruments, and percussion instruments. The lyre was a stringed instrument that looked like a small harp. It had only a few strings, which were plucked to make music. The trumpet was a wind instrument made from an animal's horn or from silver. The timbrel was a percussion instrument that looked like a tambourine. It was made with a piece of animal skin stretched over a wooden hoop.

NILE RIVER

The Nile River is 2,500 miles (4,025 km) long. It flows from high in the mountains in central Africa, through Egypt, and into the Mediterranean Sea. The water runs from south to north.

Egypt is called the gift of the Nile because the Nile River supplies Egypt with the soil and water the people need to survive. The people fish in the

The Nile River

Nile River and grow crops along its banks. Boats carry goods up and down the Nile.

The Nile usually overflows its banks in September, October, and November. When the water returns to its normal level, it leaves rich soil behind. That soil is good for growing vegetables and other crops.

When famine struck other areas, Egypt usually had food because the Nile River provided water. Abraham traveled to Egypt during a famine (Genesis 12:10), and Jacob sent his sons to Egypt for food when there was a famine (Genesis 43:1–2). When Joseph lived in Egypt, the Nile didn't flood for seven years. God showed Joseph how to store food so that the people would live.

Because the Nile was so important to them, the Egyptians worshiped it as the source of life. They believed that the Nile River flooded each year because their god Isis shed a tear. In the first plague God turned the Nile to blood, showing that he, not the Nile, gave life.

NOMADS

Nomads are people who travel from place to place instead of having a permanent home. Abraham, Isaac, and Jacob were nomads. The Israelites spent 40 years as nomads in the desert.

Life for nomads was hard. Very little rain fell in most parts of Canaan, so water and food were hard to find.

Water from springs was known as "living water." Sometimes people dug into the ground to find water. If they found water, they built a well.

Nomads lived in goatskin tents. They camped near a well or another water supply. When the water and plants for the animals were gone, they packed up their tents and moved on. During the time of the judges, nomads often raided Israel looking for food.

The nomads usually had herds of goats or sheep. The goats were smaller than the goats we're familiar with. They had long, black-brown hair and long horns, and their ears were long and floppy. The sheep were mostly white, but some had black or brown legs and heads.

The nomad men probably were about 5 feet, 7 inches tall, and the women were several inches shorter. Their skin was tan, and they had long black hair. The women sometimes braided their hair, and the men usually had beards.

Nomads

PASSOVER

God commanded the Israelites to celebrate the Passover each year to help them remember how God had rescued them from the Egyptians.

To celebrate the Passover, each Israelite family killed an unblemished (perfect) lamb. They sprinkled the lamb's blood on the doorframe of their house. Then they roasted the lamb, being careful not to break any of its bones. On the day of Passover families, wearing their traveling clothes, met together at sundown. The father began the meal with a prayer. Before the family began to eat, the son asked his father, "Why is this night different from all other nights?" The father told the story of how God had brought the Israelites out of Egypt after the first Passover. After the father finished telling the story, the family ate a meal of roasted lamb, unleavened bread (bread without yeast), and bitter herbs. Then the family sang songs from Psalms 113–118. They burned all of the leftover food.

Each part of the Passover feast helped the Israelites remember and understand what God had done to bring them out of Egypt. The lamb had been the substitute for the Israelites' firstborn sons. The unleavened bread helped the people remember that they had left Egypt in a hurry and hadn't had time for their bread to rise. The bitter herbs reminded them of how bitter and hard slavery in Egypt had been. The blood on the doorframe reminded the people that God had "passed over" the houses with blood on the doorframes. The traveling clothes reminded the people of their journey out of Egypt.

Jewish families still celebrate the Passover each year in March or April.

PHARAOH

Pharaoh was the title given to Egyptian kings. Pharaohs were believed to be descended from the gods and were thought to become gods themselves after death.

The word *pharaoh* means "the great house." Because the pharaoh owned all of the land, buildings, animals—and even the people—he was the richest person in Egypt. He was the lawgiver and the chief priest. He was also the leader of the Egyptian army. No one had more power than the pharaoh.

We don't know the name of the pharaoh when Joseph was in Egypt. The pharaoh at the time of the exodus may have been Rameses II. He built many buildings and claimed to have built the store cities of Pithom and Rameses. The Bible tells us that those cities were built by Israelite slaves.

When a pharaoh died, he was buried in a pyramid, a great tomb. The things the Egyptians thought he would need in the next life—clothing, food, weapons, chariots, jewelry, and so on—were buried with him. When a new pharaoh began to rule, people began

Statue of a pharaoh

making the things that would be buried with him. Because the Egyptians buried so many items with their pharaohs, we know more about ancient Egypt than about most other ancient civilizations.

SHEPHERDS

Many Israelites were shepherds. Sheep were important because they gave the Israelites things they needed: meat, milk, and wool.

Every Israelite family owned some sheep. A family member or a village shepherd cared for those sheep. Rachel, Jacob's wife, took care of her father's sheep. David was his family's shepherd.

The shepherd roamed the land to find food and water for the flock. The

Shepherd tending his flock

flock had to be watered at least once a day. The shepherd lowered his jar into the well or cistern with a rope and then poured the water into troughs so the sheep could drink. After the sheep drank, they rested in the shade, if they could find any. The shepherd also rested before calling the sheep back together. The sheep knew their shepherd's call.

The shepherd protected the sheep from wild animals and carried a sling to throw stones at bears, wolves, lions, and other animals. The shepherd used a staff—a long stick with a hook on the end—to guide wandering sheep back to the flock or to rescue a lost lamb from a cliff.

Many shepherds played a lyre or wooden flute to calm their sheep.

SLAVES

Slaves were people who were bought or captured in a war. Children born to slave parents also belonged to the master, the head of the household. People who were very poor sometimes sold themselves as slaves. A man who had no son might adopt one of his slaves and make the slave his heir.

Slaves worked very hard. House slaves cooked, cleaned the house, and dressed their master or mistress. Some slaves worked in the fields or were bricklayers. Other slaves worked in mines or on ships. If the head of the household was kind, his slaves had decent lives. Most slaves had miserable lives because their masters treated them cruelly.

Hieroglyphic of slaves (note the bound arms)

SNAKES

Many kinds of snakes lived in Canaan and the surrounding lands. Some were not poisonous, but many were. Some desert snakes were especially dangerous. They often struck without warning and were hard to see. The sand viper and carpet viper were two common types of dangerous desert snakes.

Snakes were often connected with evil for the people of Israel. The snake was identified with Satan and with Adam and Eve's fall into sin, and snakes often represent sin in the Bible. In contrast, the people of Egypt worshiped snakes. Snakes often appear in ancient Egyptian art. During the time of Hezekiah, the Israelites fell into the trap of worshiping the bronze snake that Moses had made. The people had kept the bronze snake in the temple at Jerusalem to remind them of what God had done for them in the desert. When King Hezekiah saw the people worshiping the bronze snake, he had it destroyed.

TEMPLE FURNISHINGS

Courtyard furnishings

The altar of burnt offering (bronze altar), which had a horn at each corner, was carved from one piece of wood. The altar was covered with bronze. A horn was carved at each of the four corners from the same piece of wood, which was then covered with bronze. A bronze grate rested on a ledge halfway down on the inside of the altar. The altar was hollow so that it was light enough to carry. When the Israelites traveled in the desert,

Altar of burnt offering

the priests carried the altar with poles slipped through four rings on the sides of the altar. When the Israelites set up the Tent of Meeting, they filled the altar with sand and placed it in the tabernacle courtyard. The priests offered five kinds of sacrifices on this altar: the burnt offering, grain offering, fellowship offering, sin offering, and guilt offering.

The laver was a large bronze basin where Aaron and the priests washed their hands and feet before entering the Tent of Meeting or offering sacrifices. It stood between the Tent of Meeting and the altar of burnt offering.

The laver that was later built for the temple was large enough for 12 priests to wash themselves at the same time.

Holy Place furnishings

The altar of incense was covered with gold and had a gold horn on each corner. The priests could also carry this altar by placing poles through the rings on the sides. When the Israelites set up the

Altar of incense

Tent of Meeting, they placed this altar in the Holy Place. Each morning the priest burned holy incense in a bowl filled with hot coals. The incense—which was made from a special blend of spices—was the only kind of incense that could be burned on the altar. As the incense burned, a sweet smell filled the Tent of Meeting.

A lampstand called a menorah stood in the Tent of Meeting. It had seven lamps—a center stem and three branches on each side. The stem had four almond blossoms, and each branch had three almond blossoms. A cup filled with olive oil rested at the top of the stem and branches. Sometimes the olive oil was mixed with myrrh, cinnamon, sugar cane, and cassia to make a sweet smell. A cloth wick, made from the priests' worn-out clothes, was placed in the oil and lit.

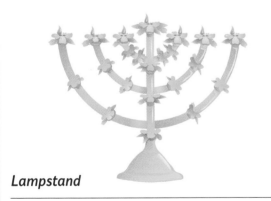

Lampstand

In the morning the priests filled the cups with enough oil to last all day and part of the night. The wicks had to be checked every two hours because they sometimes fell into the oil and burned out. If one of the side lamps went out,

the priest relit it by using the flame from one of the other lamps. The center lamp could be lit only with fire from the altar of burnt offering. When priests lit the lamps, they started on the outside and worked toward the center. The center lamp was always lit last.

Table of showbread

The table of showbread was made of acacia wood and covered with gold. A rim was molded around the tabletop. There was a gold ring on each corner of the tabletop so poles could be inserted to carry the table.

The priests stacked 12 loaves of bread, one for each tribe of Israel, on the table. They placed a golden bowl of incense on top of each stack. Each week on the Sabbath the priests put fresh bread on the table and ate the old bread. Twelve priests helped replace the bread so that the table was never empty. The table reminded the Israelites that God was the Bread of Life.

Most Holy Place furnishings

The ark of the covenant was a symbol of God's covenant with Israel. The Israelites met with God at the ark of the covenant.

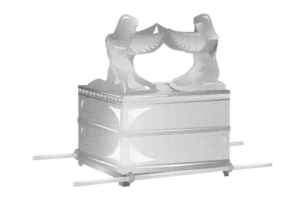

Ark of the covenant

This chest was made of acacia wood covered with gold—both inside and outside. The lid was called the mercy seat. There were two golden cherubim (winged creatures with hands and feet), one at each end of the mercy seat facing each other. The tablets of the law, the golden pot of manna, and Aaron's rod were placed inside the ark.

The ark had gold rings on the sides. When the Israelites moved, they carried the ark with long poles that fit through the rings. Nobody was supposed to touch the ark because it was holy. The ark was where God lived among his people.

TENT OF MEETING

When God's people were nomads, God traveled with them. Other gods had a specific temple to which people traveled to worship, but God had a tent that traveled with his people. This tent was called the tabernacle, and it could be carried from place to place.

At Mount Sinai God told Moses how to build the tabernacle. The Israelites gave gifts of gold, silver, fine linen, and other cloth to build it. Israel's finest craftsmen built the tabernacle out of 14 different materials. Acacia wood was the only wood used.

The tabernacle consisted of a curtain wall surrounding a courtyard. In the courtyard was the Tent of Meeting, which was divided into two sections. The priests placed the lampstand on the north and the table of showbread on the south in the Holy Place. They placed the incense altar on the west in front of the Most Holy Place (Holy of Holies). A veil with embroidered cherubim separated the Holy Place from the Most Holy Place. The ark of the covenant was placed inside the Most Holy Place. Priests entered the Most Holy Place only once a year, on the Day of Atonement.

The roof of the Tent of Meeting was probably flat. It had four layers. The top layer was made from goatskin. The second layer was made from ramskin. The third layer was tightly woven from goat hair and was waterproof.

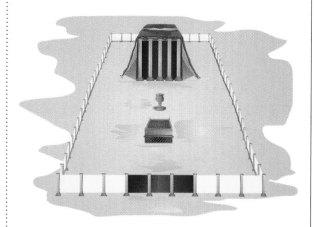

Tent of Meeting

The fourth layer was made of blue, purple, and red linen woven together into two blankets. Each blanket had five sections. Two cherubim were hand-sewn onto each section. The blankets were joined together with gold clasps.

The Tent of Meeting always faced east. A courtyard surrounded the Tent of Meeting. Curtains hung from posts to form a wall around the courtyard. The altar of burnt offering was placed between the entrance and the Tent of Meeting. The bronze basin (laver), where Aaron and the priests washed before and after sacrifices, was placed behind the altar. The Israelites could enter the courtyard to worship God, but only priests could enter the Holy Place and Most Holy Place.

The Tent of Meeting became a symbol of God dwelling with his people. God showed his presence with a pillar of smoke by day and a pillar of fire by night. When the pillar rested above the Tent of Meeting, the Israelites stopped traveling and set up camp. When the pillar moved, the people knew that it was time to move.

After the Israelites settled in the land of Canaan, God allowed King David to collect materials and King Solomon to build a permanent home, the temple.

TREES

Few trees grow in the desert because there isn't much water. The acacia is one of the few desert trees.

Acacia wood is excellent for building because it is heavy and hard. The wood dries slowly and is not easily damaged by insects. God told the Israelites to use acacia wood to make the ark of the testimony and the tabernacle furniture. Cabinetmakers still make fine furniture from acacia wood.

Nomads used acacia wood for fuel. They used the leaves to feed their cattle, and they used the tree sap for medicine and to tan leather.

Canaan had many trees, which were watered by the winter rains. In fact, the Canaanites often built shrines to their gods near large trees. Canaan's forests were part of the richness of the Promised Land God gave to the Israelites. Sycamore, oak, pine, fir, cedar, and other trees grew in Canaan. The wood from these trees was used for firewood, for building, and for making tools and furniture.

Trees that were important to the Israelites included olive trees, fig trees, and palm trees.

Olive trees are usually 30–40 feet (9–12 meters) tall. The Israelites pressed olives to make olive oil.

Full-grown **fig trees** are usually 10–15 feet tall. In the summer the fig tree has thick leaves that provide a lot of shade. The branches grow in all directions and bend downward because the leaves are so heavy. The leaves fall off during the winter rains. The fig tree bears fruit three times a year, but the August figs are the best. People eat

HOLY LAND AND SINAI

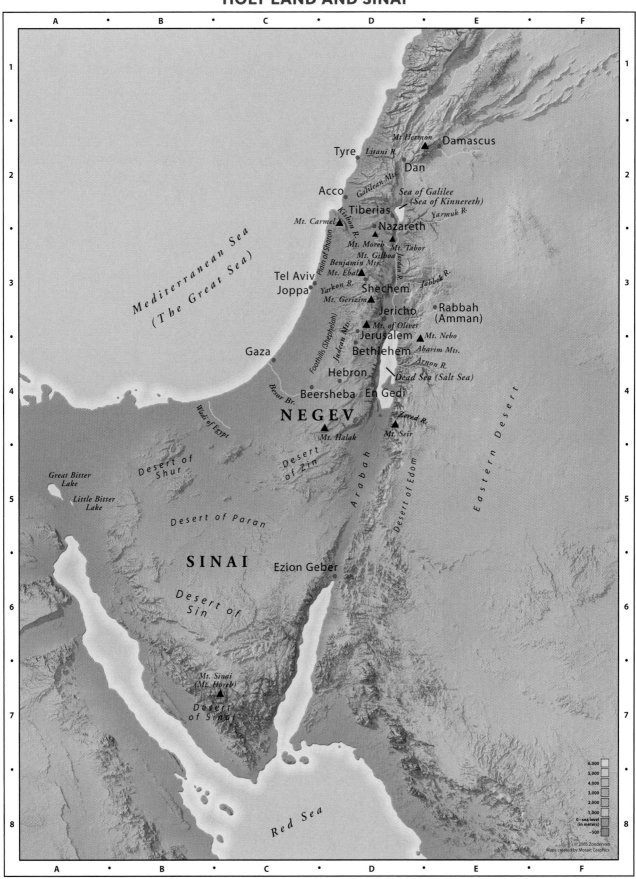

Mt Hermon
Damascus
Tyre
Litani R.
Dan
Acco
Galilean Mts.
Sea of Galilee
(Sea of Kinnereth)
Tiberias
Yarmuk R.
Mt. Carmel
Nazareth
Kishon R.
Mt. Moreh
Mt. Tabor
Mt. Gilboa
Benjamin Mts.
Jordan R.
Plain of Sharon
Mt. Ebal
Tel Aviv
Shechem
Jabbok R.
Joppa
Yarkon R.
Mt. Gerizim
Jericho
Rabbah
(Amman)
Mediterranean Sea
(The Great Sea)
Mt. of Olives
Jerusalem
Mt. Nebo
Foothills (Shephelah)
Bethlehem
Abarim Mts.
Judean Mts.
Gaza
Arnon R.
Hebron
Dead Sea (Salt Sea)
Beersheba
En Gedi
Besor Br.
NEGEV
Zered R.
Wadi of Egypt
Mt. Halak
Mt. Seir
Arabah
Great Bitter
Lake
Desert
of
Shur
Desert
of Zin
Eastern Desert
Little Bitter
Lake
Desert of Paran
Desert of Edom
SINAI
Ezion Geber
Desert of
Sin
Mt. Sinai
(Mt. Horeb)
Desert
of Sinai
Red Sea

6,000
5,000
4,000
3,000
2,000
1,000
0 ~ sea level
(in meters)
-500

© 2005 Zondervan
Maps created by Mosaic Graphics

EXODUS AND CONQUEST OF CANAAN

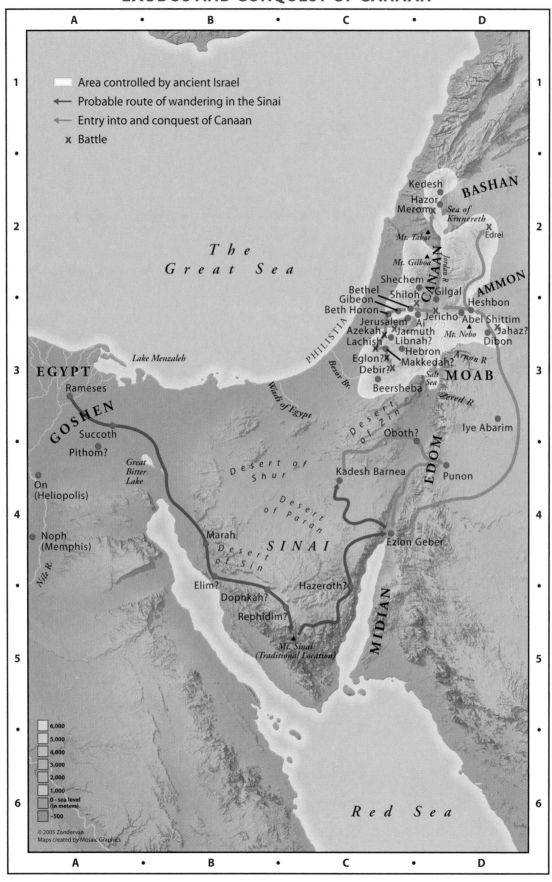

Area controlled by ancient Israel
Probable route of wandering in the Sinai
Entry into and conquest of Canaan
x Battle

BASHAN

Kedesh
Hazor
Merom x
Sea of Kinnereth
x Edrei

Mt. Tabor

CANAAN

Mt. Gilboa

Jordan R.

Shechem
Bethel
Gibeon   Shiloh   Gilgal   AMMON
Beth Horon   Heshbon
                            Jericho x Abel   Shittim
Jerusalem   Ai x Jarmuth   Jahaz?
Azekah   Mt. Nebo   Dibon
Lachish   Libnah?
            Hebron
Eglon?   Makkedah?   Arnon R.
Debir?   MOAB
            Salt
Beersheba   Sea

PHILISTIA

Besor Br.

EGYPT
Rameses

GOSHEN
Succoth
Pithom?

On
(Heliopolis)

Lake Menzaleh

Wadi of Egypt

Desert of Zin

Oboth?

Iye Abarim

EDOM   Punon

Noph
(Memphis)

Nile R.

Great
Bitter
Lake

Desert of
Shur

Kadesh Barnea

Desert of
Paran

Marah

Desert
of Sin

SINAI

Ezion Geber

Elim?

Hazeroth?

Dophkah?

MIDIAN

Rephidim?

Mt. Sinai
(Traditional Location)

6,000
5,000
4,000
3,000
2,000
1,000
0 - sea level
(in meters)
-500

© 2005 Zondervan
Maps created by Mosaic Graphics

Red Sea

The
Great Sea

LAND OF THE TWELVE TRIBES

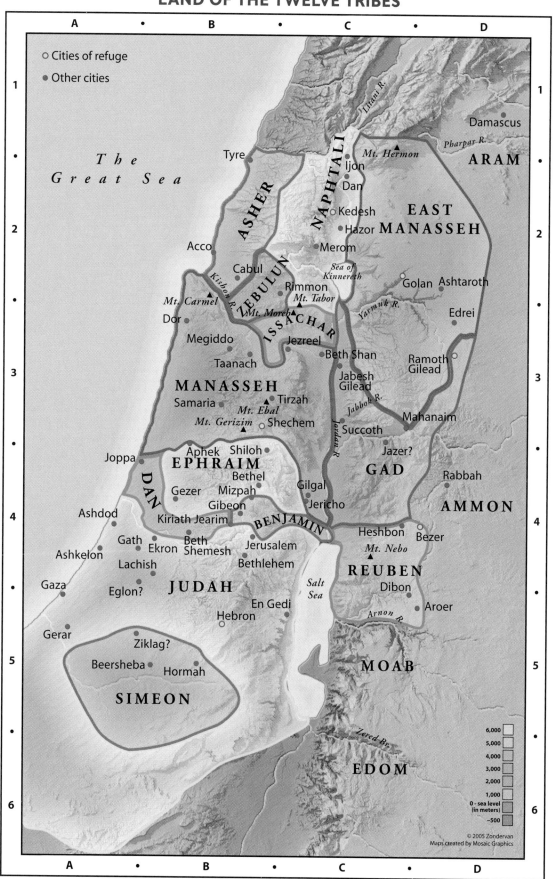

Cities of refuge
Other cities

The Great Sea

Damascus
Pharpar R.
ARAM

Tyre
Litani R.
Mt. Hermon
Ijon
Dan
ASHER
NAPHTALI
Kedesh
Hazor
EAST
MANASSEH

Acco
Merom
Cabul
Kishon R.
ZEBULUN
Sea of Kinnereth
Golan
Ashtaroth
Mt. Carmel
Rimmon
Mt. Tabor
ISSACHAR
Mt. Moreh
Yarmuk R.
Edrei
Dor
Megiddo
Jezreel
Beth Shan
Ramoth Gilead
Taanach
Jabesh Gilead
Jabbok R.
MANASSEH
Samaria
Tirzah
Mt. Ebal
Mahanaim
Mt. Gerizim
Shechem
Succoth
Jordan R.

Joppa
Aphek
Shiloh
EPHRAIM
Bethel
Jazer?
GAD
Gezer
Mizpah
Gilgal
Rabbah
Gibeon
Jericho
Ashdod
Kiriath Jearim
BENJAMIN
AMMON
Gath
Beth Shemesh
Jerusalem
Heshbon
Bezer
Ekron
Mt. Nebo
Ashkelon
Bethlehem
Lachish
Salt Sea
REUBEN
Gaza
Eglon?
JUDAH
Dibon
En Gedi
Aroer
Gerar
Hebron
Arnon R.

Ziklag?
MOAB
Beersheba
Hormah
SIMEON

Zered Br.
EDOM

DAN

6,000
5,000
4,000
3,000
2,000
1,000
0 – sea level
(in meters)
–500

© 2005 Zondervan
Maps created by Mosaic Graphics

KINGDOMS OF DAVID AND SOLOMON

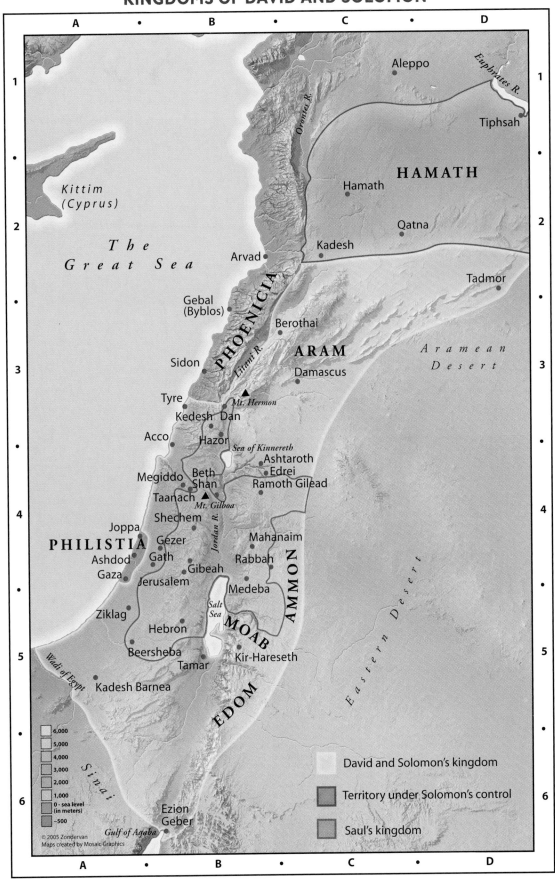

Aleppo

Euphrates R.

Tiphsah

HAMATH

Hamath

Qatna

Kittim
(Cyprus)

Kadesh

Tadmor

*The
Great Sea*

Arvad

Gebal
(Byblos)

Berothai

PHOENICIA

Litani R.

ARAM

*Aramean
Desert*

Sidon

Damascus

Tyre

Mt. Hermon

Kedesh Dan

Acco

Hazor

Sea of Kinnereth

Megiddo

Beth
Shan

Ashtaroth
Edrei

Taanach

Mt. Gilboa

Ramoth Gilead

Shechem

Jordan R.

Joppa

Mahanaim

PHILISTIA

Gezer

Ashdod

Gath

Rabbah

Gaza

Gibeah

AMMON

Jerusalem

Medeba

Eastern Desert

Ziklag

*Salt
Sea*

Hebron

MOAB

Wadi of Egypt

Beersheba

Kir-Hareseth

Tamar

Kadesh Barnea

EDOM

6,000
5,000
4,000
3,000
2,000
1,000
0 - sea level
(in meters)
-500

Sinai

David and Solomon's kingdom

Territory under Solomon's control

Ezion
Geber

Saul's kingdom

Gulf of Aqaba

© 2005 Zondervan
Maps created by Mosaic Graphics

KINGDOMS OF ISRAEL AND JUDAH

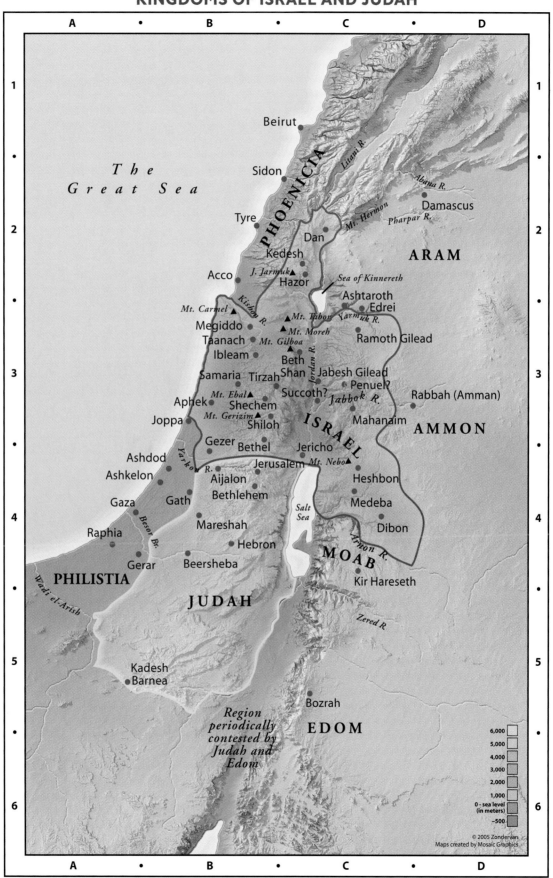

The Great Sea

Beirut

Sidon

PHOENICIA

Litani R.

Abana R.

Damascus

Mt. Hermon

Pharpar R.

ARAM

Tyre

Dan

Kedesh

Acco

J. Jarmuk ▲

Hazor

Sea of Kinnereth

Ashtaroth

Edrei

Mt. Carmel ▲

Kishon R.

▲ Mt. Tabor

Yarmuk R.

Megiddo

▲ Mt. Moreh

Ramoth Gilead

Taanach

▲ Mt. Gilboa

Ibleam

Beth Shan

Jabesh Gilead

Samaria

Tirzah

Jordan R.

Succoth?

Penuel?

Mt. Ebal ▲

Jabbok R.

Rabbah (Amman)

Aphek

Shechem

Joppa

Mt. Gerizim ▲

Shiloh

ISRAEL

Mahanaim

AMMON

Gezer

Bethel

Jericho

Ashdod

Yarkon R.

Jerusalem

Mt. Nebo ▲

Heshbon

Ashkelon

Aijalon

Medeba

Gaza

Gath

Bethlehem

Salt Sea

Dibon

Raphia

Besor Br.

Mareshah

Arnon R.

Gerar

Hebron

MOAB

Wadi el-Arish

Beersheba

Kir Hareseth

PHILISTIA

JUDAH

Zered R.

Kadesh Barnea

Bozrah

Region periodically contested by Judah and Edom

EDOM

6,000
5,000
4,000
3,000
2,000
1,000
0 - sea level (in meters)
-500

© 2005 Zondervan
Maps created by Mosaic Graphics

PROPHETS IN ISRAEL AND JUDAH

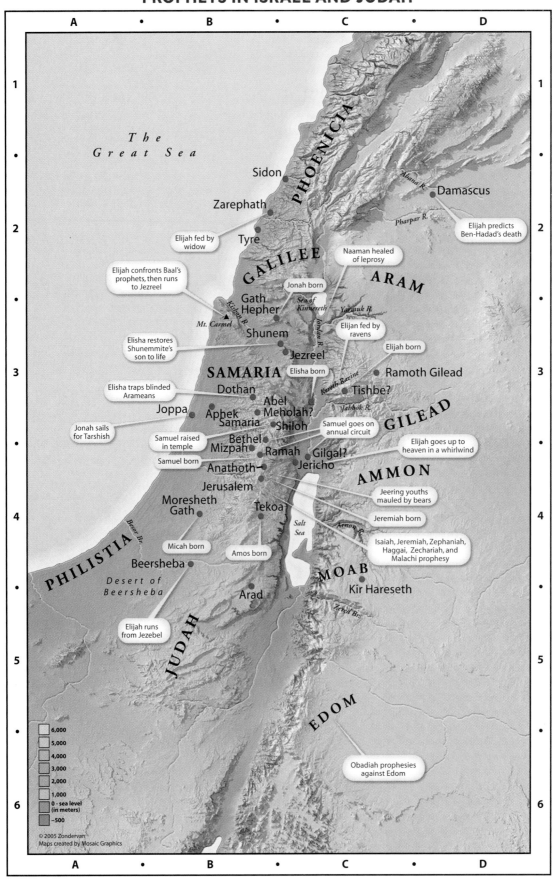

The Great Sea

Sidon

Zarephath

PHOENICIA

Abana R.

Damascus

Tyre

Elijah fed by widow

Pharpar R.

Elijah predicts Ben-Hadad's death

GALILEE

Naaman healed of leprosy

ARAM

Elijah confronts Baal's prophets, then runs to Jezreel

Jonah born

Gath Hepher

Sea of Kinnereth

Mt. Carmel

Kishon R.

Yarmuk R.

Elijah fed by ravens

Shunem

Jordan R.

Elisha restores Shunemmite's son to life

Jezreel

Elijah born

Elisha born

Ramoth Gilead

SAMARIA

Dothan

Kerith Ravine

Tishbe?

Elisha traps blinded Arameans

Abel Meholah?

Jabbok R.

GILEAD

Joppa

Aphek

Samaria

Shiloh

Samuel goes on annual circuit

Jonah sails for Tarshish

Bethel

Samuel raised in temple

Mizpah

Ramah

Gilgal?

Elijah goes up to heaven in a whirlwind

Samuel born

Anathoth

Jericho

AMMON

Jerusalem

Jeering youths mauled by bears

Moresheth Gath

Tekoa

Salt Sea

Arnon R.

Jeremiah born

Micah born

Amos born

Isaiah, Jeremiah, Zephaniah, Haggai, Zechariah, and Malachi prophesy

Beersheba

Beçor Br.

MOAB

PHILISTIA

Desert of Beersheba

Arad

Kir Hareseth

Zered Br.

JUDAH

Elijah runs from Jezebel

EDOM

6,000
5,000
4,000
3,000
2,000
1,000
0 - sea level (in meters)
-500

Obadiah prophesies against Edom

© 2005 Zondervan
Maps created by Mosaic Graphics

ASSYRIAN AND BABYLONIAN EMPIRES

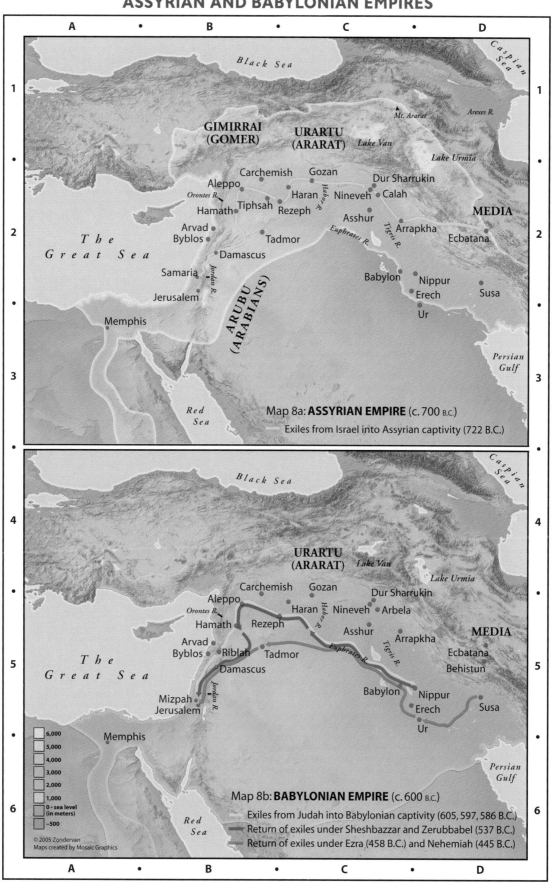

Map 8a: **ASSYRIAN EMPIRE** (c. 700 B.C.)

Exiles from Israel into Assyrian captivity (722 B.C.)

Map 8b: **BABYLONIAN EMPIRE** (c. 600 B.C.)

Exiles from Judah into Babylonian captivity (605, 597, 586 B.C.)
Return of exiles under Sheshbazzar and Zerubbabel (537 B.C.)
Return of exiles under Ezra (458 B.C.) and Nehemiah (445 B.C.)

© 2005 Zondervan
Maps created by Mosaic Graphics

HOLY LAND IN THE TIME OF JESUS

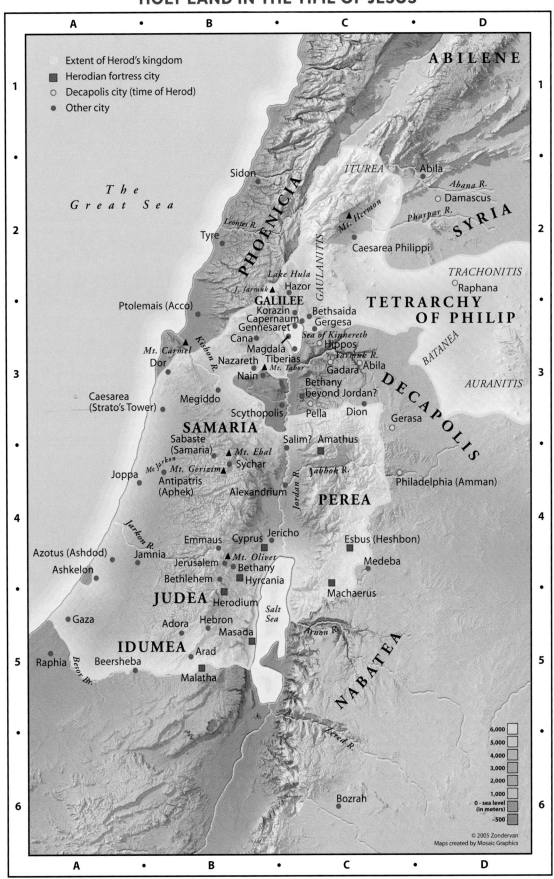

Legend:
- Extent of Herod's kingdom
- ■ Herodian fortress city
- ○ Decapolis city (time of Herod)
- ● Other city

ABILENE

The Great Sea

Sidon

PHOENICIA

ITUREA

Abila

Abana R.

○ Damascus

SYRIA

Leontes R.

Tyre

▲ *Mt. Hermon*

Pharpar R.

Caesarea Philippi

GAULANITIS

Lake Hula

J. Jarmuk ▲ Hazor

GALILEE

TRACHONITIS

○ Raphana

Korazin

Capernaum • Bethsaida
Gennesaret • Gergesa

TETRARCHY
OF PHILIP

Ptolemais (Acco)

Cana

Sea of Kinhereth

○ Hippos

BATANEA

Magdala

Nazareth Tiberias

Yarmuk R.

Nain

▲ *Mt. Tabor*

Gadara • Abila

AURANITIS

▲ *Mt. Carmel*

Dor

Kishon R.

Bethany
beyond Jordan?

○ Pella

DECAPOLIS

Caesarea
(Strato's Tower)

Megiddo

Dion

○ Gerasa

Scythopolis

SAMARIA

Salim? • Amathus

Sabaste
(Samaria)

▲ *Mt. Ebal*
Sychar

Me Jarkon

▲ *Mt. Gerizim* ▲

Joppa

Antipatris
(Aphek)

Jordan R.

Jabbok R.

○ Philadelphia (Amman)

Alexandrium

PEREA

Jarkon R.

Emmaus • Cyprus • Jericho

Esbus (Heshbon) ■

Azotus (Ashdod)

Jamnia

Jerusalem ▲ *Mt. Olivet*
Bethany

Medeba

Ashkelon

Bethlehem ■ Hyrcania

*Salt
Sea*

Machaerus ■

JUDEA Herodium ■

● Gaza

Adora • Hebron

Arnon R.

IDUMEA

Masada ■

Arad

Raphia

Beersheba

NABATEA

Besor Br.

Malatha ■

Zered R.

Bozrah

Elevation scale (in meters):
- 6,000
- 5,000
- 4,000
- 3,000
- 2,000
- 1,000
- 0 - sea level (in meters)
- −500

© 2005 Zondervan
Maps created by Mosaic Graphics

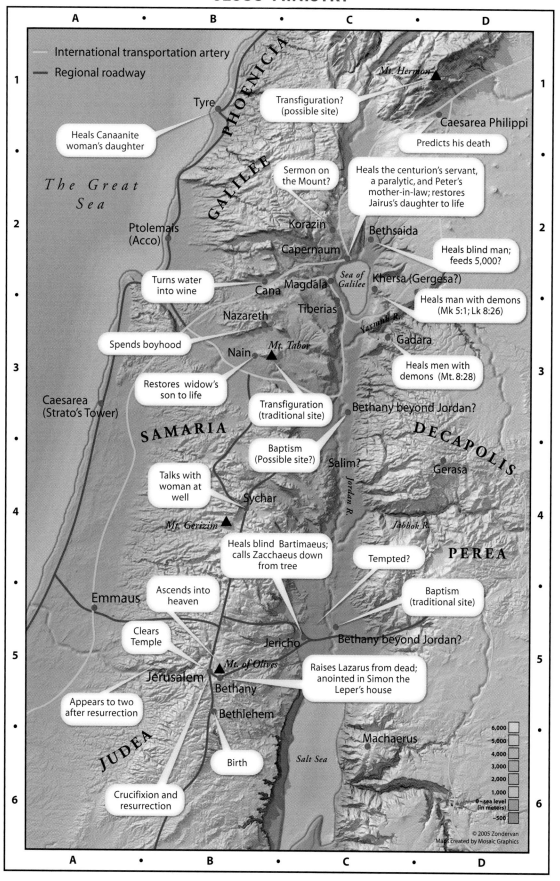

International transportation artery
Regional roadway

Mt. Hermon

Tyre

PHOENICIA

Transfiguration?
(possible site)

Caesarea Philippi

Heals Canaanite
woman's daughter

GALILEE

Predicts his death

The Great
Sea

Sermon on
the Mount?

Heals the centurion's servant,
a paralytic, and Peter's
mother-in-law; restores
Jairus's daughter to life

Ptolemais
(Acco)

Korazin

Bethsaida

Capernaum

Heals blind man;
feeds 5,000?

Turns water
into wine

Cana

Magdala

Sea of
Galilee

Khersa (Gergesa?)

Heals man with demons
(Mk 5:1; Lk 8:26)

Nazareth

Tiberias

Yarmuk R.

Gadara

Spends boyhood

Nain

Mt. Tabor

Heals men with
demons (Mt. 8:28)

Restores widow's
son to life

Transfiguration
(traditional site)

Bethany beyond Jordan?

DECAPOLIS

Caesarea
(Strato's Tower)

SAMARIA

Baptism
(Possible site?)

Salim?

Gerasa

Talks with
woman at
well

Sychar

Jordan R.

Jabbok R.

Mt. Gerizim

PEREA

Heals blind Bartimaeus;
calls Zacchaeus down
from tree

Tempted?

Emmaus

Ascends into
heaven

Baptism
(traditional site)

Clears
Temple

Jericho

Bethany beyond Jordan?

Mt. of Olives

Jerusalem

Bethany

Raises Lazarus from dead;
anointed in Simon the
Leper's house

Appears to two
after resurrection

Bethlehem

Machaerus

JUDEA

Birth

Salt Sea

6,000
5,000
4,000
3,000
2,000
1,000
0—sea level
(in meters)
−500

Crucifixion and
resurrection

© 2005 Zondervan
Maps Created by Mosaic Graphics

Timeline

(1915–1805)

(2006–1859)

(2066–1886)

(2166–1991)

2200 2100 2000 1900 1800 1700 1600 1500 1400

? ? ? ?

Early History

The Patriarchs

The Journey to Canaan

The Promised Land

													B.C.	A.D.			
1300	1200	1100	1000	900	800	700	600	500	400	300	200	100		100	200	300	400

meaning

Family Tree

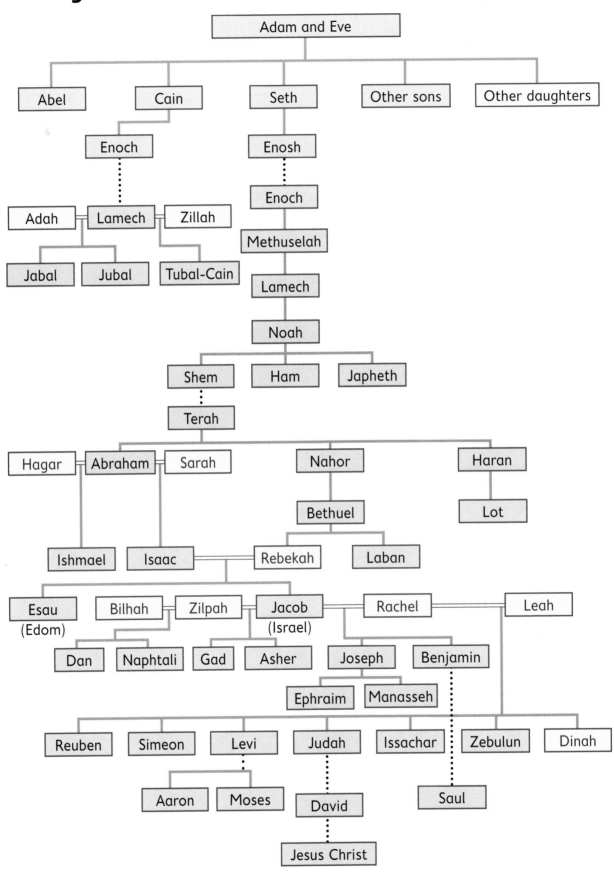

Walking With God and His People GRADE 3